Joseph Priestley in Calne

Norman Beale
MA, MD

It's for Elaine, is this

First published in the United Kingdom in 2008 for the author by
The Hobnob Press, PO Box 1838, East Knoyle, Salisbury SP3 6FA
© Norman Beale

British Library Cataloguing in Publication Data
A catalogue record for this book is available from the British Library.

ISBN 978-0-946418-81-7
Typeset in 12/15 pt Scala ; typesetting and origination by John Chandler
Printed in Great Britain by Salisbury Printing Company Ltd, Salisbury

Contents

JOSEPH PRIESTLEY IN 1783 (AGED 50) (Courtesy of the Royal Society Library, London).
Painted by Henry Fuseli (Füssli) (1741-1825), English artist of Swiss origin. Priestley was staying with his friend, Johnson, in London, just three years after leaving Calne. It is the only portrait of Priestley that shows his whole figure and is timely for this book. His eldest son, Joseph, thought it 'a marked and strong likeness of my father'.

Foreword

CALNE'S HISTORY is much tied up with that of Bowood House and the Shelburne/Lansdowne family. The story of how Joseph Priestley came to Calne and what he did in the town is a case in point and it is thanks to the huge generosity of the present Marquis of Lansdowne, and his curator Dr. Kate Fielden, that this book appears. Much of its content is, I think, new. Its focus is intended to be the seven years that Priestley and his family lived in Calne while he was employed by the second Lord Shelburne (later First Marquis of Lansdowne). Most of the chapters therefore cover, each, one of these years, 1773 to 1780 inclusive. They would, of course, be meaningless if taken totally out of context and are therefore sandwiched between a sketchy outline of the earlier and later eras of Priestley's long and busy life.

There is, now, one outstanding record of Priestley's life – the biography by Robert E Schofield. This is in two volumes: *The enlightenment of Joseph Priestley* covers his birth until 1773 and *The enlightened Joseph Priestley* picks up the story at 1773 and continues until his death (both fully referenced in the text herein). The second of these appeared only in 2004. Schofield, a professional historian of science at Iowa State University in America, spent over 40 years studying Priestley. He has produced an authorative record that is now the standard reference work. However, in trying to include everything, Schofield eschewed the 'popular' biography that, by his own admission, Priestley 'deserves'. This is not it; my own mission is much more parochial.

Everyone in Calne will tell you that Priestley discovered oxygen while living in the town. Many will then add, wrongly, that he found it bubbling up from 'Doctor's Pond' – 'behind Somerfields'. And while linking Priestley to his discovery of oxygen is correct, few will know that during his association with Lord Shelburne, and while living in Calne, he also discovered ammonia, nitrous oxide and sulphur dioxide. I hope that this book can raise Priestley's 'Calne' profile. That readers will find, finally, that they know more about the man and about his family; that their knowledge of local history will be a little more accurate; that Priestley School and Priestley Grove mean more; that they can have a jolly good gossip. I have therefore tried to make the content much more human if not a 'soap'. I must do the opposite to Schofield; apologise that this is not an academic record. Nevertheless, I trust it is accurate as far as it goes. For the central, Calne, sections of the book I have added detailed notes and citations for those who might be interested.

Norman Beale
AUGUST 2008

Acknowledgements

F IRSTLY I MUST RECORD all Elaine's tolerance to my distracted 'absences' – "why have you been up since five and why are you wearing my dressing gown?" Then I am very grateful for all the enormous help of all the following: The Marquis of Lansdowne; Kate Fielding, curator at Bowood; the staff at Wiltshire and Swindon History Centre; Devizes Museum Library and especially Lorna Haycock; the staff at the library of the Royal Society; the staff at Calne Library; Sue Boddington; John Hurley; Pat and Sandy Maundrell; Peter Treloar; the Trustees and Friends of Calne Heritage Centre; The Doctor Williams's Library, London; Brian and Davina Kemble; Jonathan and Sarah Soar; Andrea Bashore; Brian Edwards.

My last acknowledgement must be to Robert Schofield himself. Although we have never met, I've lived so intimately with his publications that I feel I know him. Without his lifetime's dedication (and endurance of by-pass surgery, twice) the Priestley record would still be chaotically dispersed and unavailable. I have relied so much on his massive, two-volume biography (*The enlightenment of Joseph Priestley*, 1997 and *The enlightened Joseph Priestley*, 2004) that it would have become an impossible intrusion for the reader for me to cite, endlessly, his page numbers. As second best, I have tried to convince Wiltshire County Council Library service that there should be reference copies of Schofield's 'Priestley' in the county, ideally at Calne Library. If they do become available, readers will be able to see what a debt I owe him.

Earnest Young Man 1733 – 1754

T HERE HAVE LONG BEEN Priestleys in Yorkshire and in the early eighteenth century one branch of the family lived at Fieldhead near Birstall, a parish about six miles southwest of Leeds. Jonas Priestley and his first wife, Mary (Swift), had six children between March 1733 and December 1739 when Mary died. Joseph, the eldest, was born on Tuesday 13 March 1733 and is the subject of our story.

The hamlets then scattered across the hilly triangle of land between the towns of Bradford, Leeds and Wakefield were in the heart of the West Riding woollen industry. Until the industrial revolution woollen cloth making was a cottage industry and Jonas Priestley, like his father before him, was a woollen cloth dresser – a man who made his living by taking raw pieces of woollen cloth through their finishing processes in preparation for their sale. An 1800 engraving of the Priestley cottage clearly shows a large extension to the property having the very large windows characteristic of woollen trade workshops where daylight was so important. The other social bond of the area was the strong thread of non-conformist religion, supporters of which were then called 'Dissenters' because although Protestant and holding firm religious conviction, they did not belong to (dissented from) the Church of England. From 1689 they had been allowed to licence Meeting Houses or Chapels, their own places of worship and several such buildings were to become very important in the life of Joseph Priestley.

In spring 1734, when about a year old, Joseph Priestley was sent by his parents to live with his maternal grandfather. Joseph Swift was a tenant farmer at Shafton near Wakefield. Distributing children through extended families, surprising to us today, was quite common in the eighteenth century when fertile couples would have child after child with relentless rapidity and many a modest home was soon filled beyond capacity. Joseph was taken to visit his

FIELDHEAD (Courtesy of the Royal Society Library, London).
Priestley's birthplace – Fieldhead near the village of Birstall, 7 miles southwest of Leeds centre. This
image, from a photograph of a lithograph made in 1800, shows, on the right, the tall, well-lit
extension to the farmhouse; the cloth-dressing workshop of Priestley's father and grandfather.

parents occasionally but it was not until he was six, after the death of the real mother he never really knew, that he returned to Fieldhead, swapping places with some of his younger brothers. In 1741 Jonas Priestley remarried and Joseph was packed off again, this time to live with his father's sister, Sarah Keighley, and her farmer husband at nearby Heckmondwike. The Keighleys were childless after many years of marriage and Joseph was informally adopted by them at the age of 9. John Keighley was moderately wealthy and when he died, in 1745, his widow was able to continue parenting young Joseph without any financial embarrassment.

Priestley loved his aunt and she doted on him, at least until he rebelled on doctrinal issues of religion in his late teens. She early spotted that the boy was of high intelligence and sought to foster it, seeing his destiny as a Minister to an Independent congregation. Joseph was therefore sent to a succession of local schools including, probably, Batley Grammar School. 'Aunt Keighley' owned properties in Batley parish and Joseph may have been exempt from the usual fees. What is certain, however, is that he studied Latin and Greek – requirements for university entrance. Many of his devout attitudes and beliefs were acquired, though, at home. Family prayers were said twice every day and Joseph often led these. Mrs. Keighley also took her 'son' to regular prayer meetings and encouraged him to debate with visiting Ministers. And Priestley was no lazy, sluggard schoolboy: in his little free time he read many works on religion, particularly those of John Bunyan.

In 1749-50, when he was 16, Priestley was seriously ill, probably with tuberculosis. Aware that he was threatened with premature death his personal religious convictions hardened and he found solace in them. He was eventually to become a determined 'Socinian' or 'Unitarian', a member of one of the minor sects arising from the Reformation. Unitarians totally deny the 'Trinity' concept of 'God the Father, God the Son and God the Holy Ghost' that underpins other churches. God, to a Unitarian, is a simple divine being and salvation comes from following the life example of someone who was merely a man, if exceptional - Jesus Christ. The scriptures are the only real source of the 'truth'. In fact many mainstream believers fail to see how Unitarians can call themselves 'Christian' at all. The teenage Priestley's growing convictions even put him at odds with his Aunt and the elders of the Heckmondwike Chapel, who were all traditional Calvinists. But, even as a sickly youth, Priestley courageously showed the determination and single-mindedness that would always dominate his adult personality. He always made friends easily, was generally affable and cheerful but there was emotional steel running through him. An intellectual difference could easily become a personal abyss. Throughout his life his detractors would describe him as rigid, stubborn and blinkered, oblivious to the feelings of others. A man who refused to be moved from adopted attitudes and convictions would be a kinder description.

Although his health slowly improved, Priestley remained very weak and there was a family proposal that he be sent to Lisbon for the 'warm climate cure'. Thankfully this desperate, and largely futile, tactic was never needed but Priestley taught himself, very usefully, some French, Italian and German in expectation. His education was further enhanced by lessons in mathematics given by the Reverend George Haggestone, a local Dissenting Minister. At least, that was the expectation but, for once, Priestley was a reluctant pupil and Haggestone allowed the curriculum to drift, wholly, towards his pupil's innate interests in natural philosophy (which we now call science) and metaphysics (which we now call philosophy!). By 1752 Priestley's vigour was fully restored.

He was, his aunt felt, strong enough again to contemplate higher education leading to a career as a Minister. Priestley was certainly not someone to pretend, even, that he subscribed to the 39 Articles of the Church of England, however strong the motive. Therefore he could never attend any College at Oxford or Cambridge. He might have gone to a Scottish university or travelled to the continent but there was already, for non-conforming students, an established and cheaper alternative; matriculation at one of the English Dissenting Academies. In fact, as the English medieval universities languished in near irrelevance during the eighteenth century, Dissenting Academies flourished. At some the education was easily better than at Oxbridge and for a fraction of the cost. Thus, in September 1752, Priestley travelled southwest to enrol at the Academy at Daventry in Northamptonshire (between Northampton and Warwick), newly established there by the Reverend Caleb Ashworth.

Priestley's devotion to his studies as a teenager enabled him to enter the Daventry course in the third of the usual five years although he was often conscious of his deficiencies. His biggest embarrassment, in an institution where oral debate in the pursuit of 'truth' was the norm, was his stammer. This had not impinged on his private studies at home in Yorkshire but at Daventry he was forced to take some pains to try to overcome it including, even, rehearsing sermons with Ashworth himself. He made some progress, certainly, for unless under great stress, he could usually mask his disability later in life, even in the pulpit. Ashworth was also the model for what became another Priestley characteristic – his disciplined use of time. The Principal of Daventry organised his own day as clockwork; minutes, quarters and hours were obsessively regulated by the watch that was always on his desk. Priestley never became quite so fanatical but he was always convinced that scholarly activity should be segmented and organised. But despite Ashworth's love of 'order' there was certainly youthful exuberance among his students. There were parties, outbursts of horseplay, forays into the town and late-night music and singing. Likely it was at this time that Priestley learnt to play the flute. There were even flirtations with local girls. It would be surprising if Priestley didn't participate in some of these 'extra-curricular' activities but like all his carefree fellows, he soon had to mutate into the ultra-respectable community leader that was his vocation. Newly qualified ministers had to wait for invitations from congregations and Ashworth chose to pass on to Priestley one from the people of Needham Market, Suffolk (about seven miles north of Ipswich) in late 1755.

Building a Career 1755 – 1763

WHATEVER THE PROFESSION, some people flourish and succeed in their first appointment; Joseph Priestley didn't. His position at Needham Market was as assistant to the rapidly declining Minister there, John Meadows. At 79, Meadows had held the position for over 50 years. Needham was a poor, dwindling community and its Dissenters had drifted away from the services held by their jaded Minister. Although they had been pleased to hear that a young man was willing to come to them for only £40 a year they were instantly disillusioned by his preaching. Stressed by the lukewarm reception, Priestley's stammer returned: this, and his Yorkshire accent, made him difficult to understand. Then, as their new assistant Minister used the pulpit to advance his very unconventional beliefs with his usual disregard of tact, Meadows himself denounced him. Congregations shrank further and Priestley's salary was reduced. He found himself struggling to exist on barely £30 a year. At the same time he discovered that his family connections were no longer a prop: the idiosyncratic beliefs that had upset the Needham worshippers had now also permanently alienated him from his Aunt. When she died, in 1764, she was to leave him only a token of her remembrance, a silver tankard. With an income below subsistence level, with a worsening speech impediment, rejected and lonely, and trapped as a failure in his chosen profession, Priestley resorted to the only recourse open to him – to try to start a school. This, too, was a disaster and it was only a few donations from various charities that kept him alive. He used his time in writing some texts discussing fine points of religious doctrine and, to his surprise, one of these was published, by a friend, in the form of an anonymous pamphlet. This dim light in a sea of despair encouraged a further treatise and this, too, had a favourable private reception among his old friends from Daventry. In fact, knowing his predicament and seeing the waste of talent, they joined in proposing him as the languages tutor at a new Dissenting Academy at Warrington in Cheshire. Priestley was not selected but a very distant relative in Sheffield, also hearing of his difficulties, used his influence to have Priestley appointed, supposedly for a year, in September 1758, as Minister to a congregation at nearby Nantwich, just south of Crewe.

Priestley was more fortunate in Nantwich. The town, though also then in decline, was larger and he found his congregation more liberal, more tolerant of his views. They also had less difficulty with his accent and, encouraged by their hospitality, the new Minister worked hard to overcome his stammer again. His speech impediment improved but his finances didn't. Once again he tried to open a school and, this time, succeeded in attracting some pupils. For three years he taught classes of up to 30 boys, investing some of his extra income in books and some 'philosophical' instruments – an air pump and a static electrical machine. He even wrote his own book for use in English classes, a work that would later be a publishing success: 'The Rudiments of English Grammar'. His school soon had a deservedly high reputation; both his management skills and his teaching methods aroused interest and admiration.

In the summer of 1761 the post of tutor in languages at the Warrington Academy fell vacant again and this time Priestley was first choice for the post. He left Nantwich reluctantly but the move was a very favourable one, especially for his personal life. At Warrington he found 60 students enrolled in very congenial community and was given charge of one of the two new houses built specially for the residential students. In May 1762 he was ordained; motivated, perhaps, by the need for greater financial security for only five weeks later, on Wednesday 23 June 1762, he married at Wrexham. His bride was Mary, the 19-year-old daughter of Isaac Wilkinson, an iron manufacturer in the town, originally from Cumbria.

It may be simply from the expected reticence of the times that we know nothing of Priestley's courtship of Mary Wilkinson. He probably met her through her younger brother who had been one of his pupils at Nantwich and who travelled with him to Warrington. Mary was the near-perfect wife for Joseph Priestley; intelligent and tolerant, hardworking and 'greatly excelling in everything related to household affairs'. But, as we shall see, she could confront her husband successfully when she disagreed with him. Mary was a light-hearted foil to Priestley's serious intensity and was very sociable: Priestley suddenly had many more friends. And it was not long before he was a father. The Priestley's first child, a daughter they named Sarah (Sally), was born on Thursday 14 April 1763.

JOSEPH PRIESTLEY AGED 30 (Courtesy of the Royal Society Library, London).
A portrait, photographed in London in 1860, which had been in the possession of a William Hudson at Gildersome, near Leeds. Often referred to as the 'Leeds' portrait, this is misleading. At the age of 30 Priestley was one of the teaching staff at Warrington Academy and the portrait may have been prompted by his ordination or his marriage.

MARY PRIESTLEY (Courtesy of the Joseph Priestley House, Northumberland, PA., USA).
After Carl Frederick von Breda (1759-1818), Swedish painter who resided in London between about 1788 and 1796. Therefore this portrait was probably painted when Mary was in London between July 1791 and March 1794 when she was about 50. However it seems appropriate to place it alongside her husband around the time of their marriage.

Building a Reputation 1763 – 1771

P RIESTLEY WAS EQUALLY happy and successful as a tutor at the Academy. His language courses were very popular and he collected his lectures into a further book on linguistic theory, also published. He also taught oratory and criticism, seemingly reading up on the subjects one week and lecturing on them the next (in time-honoured fashion). And with a versatility that surprised even himself he also took on the teaching of history and natural history. His exemplary industry brought its reward. The trustees of the Academy recommended to the University of Edinburgh Faculty of Law, in 1764, that Priestley should receive a degree (LL.D. – Doctor of Laws) and this was awarded on 4 December. Henceforth he was 'Dr. Priestley'.

It was Priestley's growing fascination for natural philosophy – what we now call science and technology – that led to another turning point in his life. Despite his lecturing load of up to five hours every day Priestley began to spend long hours toying with the scientific apparatus that he found at Warrington. Amusement led to intrigue and an intense interest, particularly in phenomena he was able to observe after charging up electrical machines. Studying the static electricity generated by rotary friction was the most popular scientific activity of the mid eighteenth century but even so Priestley had soon made a series of observations that he found to be new and unique. At least he thought so. In trying to match his observations with those of others he was irritated and frustrated. No one had ever collected together all that was known on electricity: here was an opportunity for an enthusiast – to write a unifying history of the subject – and he grabbed it.

In the 1760s the doyen of electrical experimentation was Benjamin Franklin, another amateur, a printer and politician from Philadelphia. He was already world famous as the man who had proven, by his kite, wet string

*BENJAMIN FRANKLIN (Courtesy of the
Wellcome Library, London).
After Joseph Duplessis (1725-1802) Paris,
1778; the image on the present US $100 bill.
Priestley met Franklin in London in late 1765.
They became very close but it was a friendship
that would, later, lead Priestley into
significant difficulties with Lord Shelburne.*

and dangling key experiments, that lightning was a form of static electricity. Since Franklin was in London as Pennsylvania Agent, Priestley wangled a means of introduction and leave of absence from Warrington and set off, in late December 1765, on the expensive and uncomfortable three-day journey to London. This madcap scheme proved, in fact, to be very auspicious. The English 'electricians' John Canton and William Watson were impressed by his experiments and promptly led him, as he had hoped, to Franklin. The three 'electrical' friends were all Fellows of the Royal Society and Priestley was their guest at the meeting of the Society on Thursday 9 January 1766. There was universal approval of Priestley's idea for writing a 'history of electrical discoveries' and he was helped to acquire all the books and pamphlets that he would need. His new friends also insisted that he include, in the book, his own impressive experiments and they offered to read and correct draft chapters for him. They did even more. Admiring his original work and sensing that it would help to promote what would be a valuable book, they nominated Priestley for fellowship of the Royal Society. Charles Morton, Secretary of the Society was also a sponsor and Priestley heard that he had been elected on 12 June. The honour and the debt he owed to his new friends (presumably they also paid his £25 enrolment fee) carried him through the drudgery of the enormous editorial task he had taken on and through the double-checking of his own experiments. The book[I] was completed in a year – by March 1767. It was a huge success, going through four reprints and being translated into French and German. No serious student of electricity during the next fifty years could afford to ignore it. It also fired a life-long friendship with Joseph Johnson, who published the book at his printing house near Fleet Street. Johnson, also a young man making a name for himself and also a Dissenter, found his business so boosted by 'Electricity' that he never ever refused to print any subsequent Priestley manuscript. Priestley's own satisfaction must have been equally intense but a cold shower awaited him at home. Pressing frugality and constant hard work as 'housemother' to the students living with them had made Mary unwell and as an academic, however buoyant his career path, Priestley had very poor financial prospects. He decided to return to ministering a congregation and a notice appeared in a Leeds newspaper on 9 June 1767 that the 'Rev. Dr. Priestley' had been appointed Minister at the 'dissenting meeting house at Mill Hill in this town.'

In taking up the post of Minister at the Mill Hill Chapel at Leeds, Priestley was returning home. However he never repaired the rift with his Priestley relatives, even with his brothers and sisters. His new appointment spoke for itself; Mill Hill was the oldest and largest Dissenters' Meeting House in the city. He did, however, soon make contacts among the other Ministers in Leeds and neighbouring towns. In particular he met Theophilus Lindsey who, though the Rector of Catterick and a member of the Orthodox Church (until he reneged), was to become his closest ever friend. At first the Priestleys lived in a house south of the River Aire, in Meadow Lane. This was outside the main town itself, near to the Jacques brewery. Priestley appears to have settled into this, his third ministry, without any of the traumas that he had previously suffered, especially at Needham. Mary, too, was happier, perhaps because she was no longer responsible for all of the students who had lodged with them at Warrington. And on Sunday 24 July 1768 the couple had their first son, Joseph junior (Jos).

Restless as ever, Priestley rapidly took on many activities at Leeds. One of these was the establishment of a circulating library in the city. Whether or not this institution was his idea, he was chosen as secretary to the organising committee at its inaugural meeting in 1768. Within two years it had over 800 books on its lists and remains, today, as a memento to his civic endeavours. Not that he was solely involved in making available the literary efforts of others. He founded and edited an annual religious journal – 'The Theological Repository' – which Johnson printed for him in London. It was probably the first scholarly journal dedicated to speculative theology and certainly the first for Unitarianism. Priestley and his friends wrote most of the articles but after three years he had lost over £30 and publication ceased until he tried to revive it, many years later, in 1784. He also manned the front line of church politics. The first parliament after the restoration of the monarchy in 1660 had passed a series of laws designed to compel adherence to the established, Protestant, Church of England. Though never strictly enforced these included provisions that prevented Dissenters from holding political office, serving in the armed forces, teaching in schools, or matriculating at Oxford or Cambridge (The 'Test Acts'). Charles II himself opposed such restrictions, aimed, really, at Catholics, and tried to repeal them in 1672. His attempted moderation backfired. Parliament devised even more stipulations such as Dissenters not being allowed to be executors to a Will or even receive a legacy. Though the 'Toleration Act' during the joint reign of William and Mary did remove some of these restrictions, eighteenth century Dissenters long agitated for their full repeal. Priestley joined in, wielding, characteristically, his pen. His 'Essay on Government' was published while he was at Leeds though it must have been written largely at Warrington. Priestley had long held the view that there should be no civil authority over matters of belief and religious practice. Why, he argued, should sincere nonconformists be forced to marry in the parish church while often being denied burial rights in the churchyard on the whim of the local clergy? The persistent campaign for repeal of the 'Test Acts' in particular became strongly linked to Priestley but his writings often advanced profound general principles. Among these was the theme taken up and rephrased, famously, by Jeremy Bentham as 'the greatest good for the greatest number' - 'Utilitarianism'. And the fundamental separation of church and state, of political power having no authority to restrict religious practices or choose an 'establishment' church became, of course, the first of the ten supplementary principles (the 'amendments' forming the 'Bill of Rights') of the American Constitution of 1789.

Dissenters were not the only agitated religious group in the eighteenth century. Many establishment clergy were, themselves, unhappy with having to accept all of the mandatory 39 Articles of the Church of England. In 1771 a group including Priestley's great friend, Theophilus Lindsey, met at the Feathers Tavern in London and organised a petition seeking fundamental reform. Ultimately, this was vetoed by the Bishops in the House of Lords and its signatories, including Priestley, were left disappointed. But all the time that Priestley, a family man, was challenging the privileges of established religion, ministering to his Mill Hill congregation, setting up the Leeds library and editing his 'Repository', he was writing another important science compendium. Inspired by his success with 'Electricity' he was compiling a parallel history – of discoveries in vision, light and colours (that came to be known as his 'Optics') – as well as a seminal monograph on perspective. A yet further project, on the history of magnetism, was stillborn; after all there are only 24 hours in the day even for a polymath.

A Head Start in Chemistry

P RIESTLEY'S SCIENTIFIC INTERESTS survived his resignation as
a don and the remove away from academic life. He supervised the
printing of the second edition of his 'History of Electricity' and
performed new experiments, some of them with a Leeds surgeon. He also
made a friend of the Leeds engineer and instrument maker, Joseph Smeaton,
famous for his air pump. But Priestley knew that one of the hubs of the
scientific world was London and it became his habit to make an annual visit,
staying with Joseph Johnson, and attending meetings of the Royal Society.
Here he was soon reporting on new experiments he had been making – on
'airs'. This was his entrée into the world we now call Chemistry. He was to
dominate it for a generation.

Living next to a brewery helped rekindle his drive to experiment. He
gained permission to collect the 'air' bubbling up form the vats of fermenting
beer and from 1767 onwards he made a long study of this gas. He found it to
be 'fixable' or 'fixed' air (carbon dioxide) – so-named by the Scottish chemist,
Joseph Black, who had discovered it in 1756. Heavier than ordinary air, it
dissolved readily in water. The resultant solution was already available from
natural sources that bubbled up in spa towns in Europe, hence 'artificial
Pyrmont water' which was what Priestley chose to call it. Today we refer to it
as soda water. Priestley went on to show that the exact same gas, with the
very same properties, could be produced very simply by dribbling 'oil of vitriol'
(sulphuric acid) onto chalk. In fact he was forced to develop his own method
for producing the gas. Even before the family moved into more central Leeds
he had made himself very unpopular at the brewery; he had ruined a large vat
of beer by trying to mix the evolving carbon dioxide with ether. At first he
wrote up his observations just for the private interest and amusement of his
friends and as he became interested in other 'airs' his 'Pyrmont water'

apparatus was pushed to the back of his workbench. The true significance of his findings was brought home to him while in London, in March 1772. One afternoon he was one of the guests invited to dine with the Duke of Northumberland. The diners were all asked to taste some water that had been distilled from seawater. They all agreed that it was perfectly drinkable but flat and tasteless. Priestley immediately announced that he knew how to restore both taste and freshness. The company was intrigued and he assembled the necessary apparatus at Johnson's the next day and convinced his friends that he was right. Various samples of his 'artificial Pyrmont water' then circulated in London high society and in early April Priestley received an invitation to demonstrate his process at the Royal College of Physicians. Priestley's invention convinced what was probably a highly sceptical audience. The College kept a sample of the water for some weeks and announced that it remained fresh and free from 'noxious substances'. Priestley was so pleased with the positive response of the Physicians that he decided to publish a pamphlet. 'Directions for Impregnating Water with Fixed Air'. Dated Leeds 4 June 1772, it included a copperplate print of his apparatus and immediately sold well. Johnson, inevitably the publisher, was even able to report, within a few weeks, that it had been translated into French and was on sale in Paris. It has been well said that it was Priestley who started the soft drinks industry although it was Johann Schweppe, a German, who, having the entrepreneurial flair that Priestley lacked, took out a patent and made a fortune.

The results of all Priestley's other early explorations in chemistry were submitted to the Royal Society in early 1772. It was a very long and detailed dissertation on 'airs' – 118 pages when printed in the 'Philosophical Transactions', the official journal of the Society. It was read to fellows in four instalments – at each of the successive Thursday meetings of March 1772. Additions to the paper, referring to further experiments of summer 1772, were also read on 26 November. Overall the paper provoked more questions about gases than it answered but as a pioneering 'tour de force' this was really the point. Priestley was throwing down many shiny new pieces of a vital jigsaw puzzle that would take science many decades to fit together. 'Pneumatic chemistry' as this branch of 'natural philosophy' came to be known was kick-started by his prize-winning work. The paper was, in fact, a composite one. Any one of the main discoveries would have merited, alone, a paper worthy of the Royal Society. Priestley impressed his audience with his attention to detail and ingenious use of simple equipment. Any one of them could have obtained, if they so wished, his everyday materials, constructed his simple apparatus and repeated the experiments. He described how different gases have different solubility in water and how a constant fraction of 'common air' (atmospheric air) dissolves. 'Common air' was of particular importance, of course, since it is the 'fluid' in which most terrestrial plants and animals live, including human beings. Priestley was not a physician but believed, like all doctors at the time, that 'bad' air – miasma - was responsible for many diseases. The 'salubrity' (suitability for breathing) of the air was therefore an important question and in a few ingenious experiments he was able to show that air 'spoiled' by the presence of a mouse, or a lighted candle, trapped under a bell jar, could be 'restored' by swapping in a plant. This historic observation, lost among all the others, was perhaps the most significant. It was the beginning of a long pedigree of discoveries which would give us, eventually, our modern understanding of 'photosynthesis', the process in which plants, using light as energy source, trap carbon to turn into food and release oxygen, equally essential for all life. There was a section on the 'inflammable air' that we now call hydrogen (though confused, in places, with methane which also supports a flame). He had followed up a suggestion from Henry Cavendish (Grandson of the Second Duke of Devonshire of Chatsworth House) and studied the 'nitrous air' (nitric oxide) produced when 'spirit of nitre' (nitric acid) is dribbled onto metals. In particular he noted that when 'nitrous air' was mixed with 'common air' there was a violent reaction making red fumes. Moreover, the resultant mixture was reduced in bulk in proportion to the 'purity' of the common air sample. Here, he saw, was a new means of assessing the 'salubrity' (fitness for respiration) of any air sample: an improvement that did not require the martyrdom of mice. He reported his discovery of 'acid air' (hydrogen chloride) and of a gas, which he did not name, given off by hot 'saltpetre' (potassium nitrate). The latter 'air', he noted, supported a candle flame – indeed 'the flame was increased'. This was, he wrote, a 'very extraordinary and important' finding that 'may lead to considerable discoveries.' He was absolutely right. Although he had not yet 'discovered' oxygen, for he glossed over his observation and didn't understand its implications, he had been the first to have witnessed its unique power.

Headhunted 1771 & 1772

BY 1771, AT THE AGE OF 38, Priestley's was a well-known name in several national spheres of influence and he began to be headhunted. The first instance, a very fast-moving one, occurred in the first ten days of December 1771. Around the first of the month Priestley received, out of the blue, a letter from William Eden (Lord Auckland) postmarked London. Although its arrival was a surprise and its contents even more so, Priestley responded almost at once. He seemed not to hesitate even though a positive decision would mean resigning as Minister at Mill Hill and abandoning his young family - another boy, William, had been born on 7 May 1771. The post offered was on an oceanic exploration and therefore for a considerable time, perhaps for years or, even, for ever, for the position was not without danger. And, on a more mundane level, he was not even qualified for the job. James Cook's first expedition to the South Seas and Australasia (1768 – 1771) on the 'Endeavour' had been so successful that the Admiralty Board decided, in September 1771, to ask him to lead a second voyage. Cook's instructions this time were to 'find rest and refitting stations for ships rounding Cape Horn' but it was well understood that he would sail on west to further explore the 'southern continent'. The Admiralty also indicated, as was its usual practice, that suitable individuals or representatives of the Royal Society could travel on the expedition, at their own expense, in order to study and collect specimens of minerals, plants and animals. A young man of independent means called Joseph Banks had filled this scientific role on Cook's first expedition; he, and his personal party of eight chosen assistants. Banks leapt at the invitation to lead another exciting forage under Cook and began to recruit a further team; this time 15 people besides himself. Then he heard that the Astronomer Royal, Neville Maskelyne, was proposing that two more 'scientists' be appointed to make astronomical observations to test new navigational instruments. Banks, whose wealth was superseded only by his ego, immediately assumed that he, himself, had the right to make these two further appointments. The letter inviting Priestley to join the ship was one result. But the hasty invitation proved to be a false start. Even as Priestley's equally ill-considered acceptance was on its way to London, Banks' arrogance had provoked a backlash from the proper authorities and it was clear by 5 December that his nominations were going to be obstructed. Banks was forced to write to Priestley himself. He appears to have tried to hide his embarrassment behind a smokescreen; that he thought the orthodox clergymen who, as Professors at Oxford and Cambridge, sat on the Board of Longitude of the Admiralty, would veto Priestley's recruitment because of his dissenting religious beliefs. Priestley was somewhat flustered and wrote to Eden, on 10 December, that he regretted 'seeming to jump at a proposal that was never made to me'. In fact Banks' whole involvement with the project also collapsed. In a spasm of bad temper when the Admiralty dismantled the modifications he had insisted on making to Cook's ship (which had made it unstable and unseaworthy) he announced his decision not to go on the voyage after all. Some small compensation was available for Priestley. The Admiralty, sharing the rumour that his 'Pyrmont water' could prevent scurvy, instructed Cook to try it on his second voyage. So, if Priestley didn't get to go with Cook his water did – or at least it should have done. There is actually no evidence that the reactionary Cook ever tried it. Another successful Yorkshireman, he was as stubborn as Priestley and kept up his faith in fresh water and iron discipline.

In the midst of all this excitement, Priestley had also received a letter from Dr. Richard Price, a well-known radical writer.

RICHARD PRICE (Courtesy of the Wellcome Library, London).
Line engraving, T. Holloway after Benjamin West (1738-1820). It was Price, a close friend of both men, who recommended Priestley to Lord Shelburne in 1772.

Price, Unitarian Minister to a Dissenter congregation in north London, was originally from South Wales. Now in middle age – at nearly 50 – he had made a reputation as a preacher, publisher of sermons, and as one of the first demographers and statisticians, wielding a mathematical brilliance that had led to his election as a Fellow of the Royal Society. Price's letter was probably the first indication to Priestley that the position on Cook's ship was not in Banks' purview but it also contained an enigmatic enquiry that lacked context. Did Priestley know of any Dissenting Ministers who were well read in history, languages and philosophy and who would be qualified to help educate two young children? There is no record of Priestley having given the matter any real thought while a world cruise was on the cards or while his 'Pyrmont water' experiments were reaching such a pleasing culmination. If he had known the whole story he might have given it more priority. Price had been asked to put out such feelers by William Petty, second Lord Shelburne. This 34-year-old Whig statesman had grown up in Ireland and been educated at Oxford. He had served with distinction in the Seven Years War and then been elected as an MP. His father had died shortly thereafter however, and he succeeded to the House of Lords, in 1761, before he could take his Commons seat. He was given ministerial office very quickly and headed several departments of state until his political career took a dive in the late 1760s. He was always sympathetic to the causes of the American colonists and knew Benjamin Franklin well. He had married

Lady Sophia Carteret in 1765 and the union had given him two sons. Tragically their mother had died in 1771 and he was suddenly a single parent.

Shelburne and Price had become friends in 1769 and after his bereavement the aristocrat had found solace in some of Price's published religious texts. Then, on the point of

WILLIAM PETTY, 2ND LORD SHELBURNE AND, FROM 1784, 1ST MARQUIS OF LANS-DOWNE. (Courtesy of the Trustees of the Bowood collection.) This portrait, of 1791, by French artist Jean-Laurent Mosnier (1743-1808), from a later era than when Shelburne employed Priestley, and after his service to the country as Prime Minister, is, somehow, redolent of his personality.

leaving for a continental tour to further distract himself from his grief, Shelburne had asked Price to 'uncover' a suitable person to be an intellectual companion and guide him in arranging the education of his boys. He was also anxious to have an ear to Dissenter politics. Price failed to see himself in the role, or perhaps thought better of it, and, taking the request literally rather than as a subtle invitation aimed at himself, went headhunting. When Priestley also failed to take the bait, Price threw away the kid gloves. By June 1772 he was actively promoting Priestley to Shelburne and agreed to write a more explicit letter to Leeds asking his young friend to consider the position. The reply[2] would have arrived at Newington Green a few days after 2 July. Priestley clearly saw himself as well qualified to supervise the tuition of Shelburne's sons:

> I flatter myself, indeed, that I might render his Lordship some service with respect to the education of his children, as that is a subject to which I have given very particular attention, and with respect to which I have had a good deal of experience . . .

He was very dubious, however, that he suited some of the other roles that Shelburne envisaged:

> It is true that my reading and studies have had as great a range as, I believe, those of most people; but I imagine that the information which his Lordship might occasionally want would relate chiefly to things of a political nature, which I have not particularly studied . . .

He was also very concerned that the job description implied that, as constant companion to Shelburne, he would have to abandon Mary and the children:

> I am so habituated to domestic life, and am so happy at home, that it is not possible I should receive any compensation for not living with my family.

Priestley arranged these arguments in a logical sequence in his long letter to Price but his conclusion, strangely, was in the opening paragraph. Price would already have read:

I think myself exceedingly honoured by the . . . very favourable opinion which Lord Shelburne's proposal implies . . . but I really do think it would not be in my power to render his Lordship any service equivalent to the recompense . . .

However, as if to prove how tempted Priestley was, nevertheless, to leave his Leeds congregation, Price was to read, at the very end of the letter, a request that he

. . . represent to Lord Shelburne my sentiments on the general view of his Lordship's proposal. If he should think that the obstacles I have mentioned may be removed in a manner consistent with his own views, he shall find me very ingenious and explicit on the subject.

Shelburne saw his chance and made his move. On 22 August 1772 he was on Priestley's doorstep in Leeds. Three days later Priestley again wrote to Price[3]

On Saturday last Lord Shelburne, as you gave me reason to expect, called upon me, and he explained and enforced his proposal in such a manner that I own I am much disposed to comply with it. He said he never thought of settling upon me less than £200 per annum for life, and would do as much more as you and myself should think reasonable. So we agreed upon the sum mentioned in your letter, £250. Besides, I am to have a house adjoining his own in town, and another very near his seat in the country. If, however, we should like the situation in the country, it is probable we shall keep to it, myself only attending his Lordship when he shall require my attendance in London. He gives me what time I think proper to consider his proposals . . . I think, however, it will answer no good end, either to keep his Lordship in suspense, or to stay long here after I am determined to go.

Doubts remained, however. Perhaps Mary was unhappy with the prospect of living alone with the children even if it was only for part of each year. Priestley wrote to ask the urgent advice of someone who was now one of his closest friends, Benjamin Franklin: what should he do? Franklin didn't actually give a verdict[4] but referred his fellow philosopher to a means of arriving at a 'prudential' answer by using one of his own favourite tricks when faced with difficult decisions – 'moral algebra'. Priestley should fold a piece of paper vertically and put 'pro-Shelburne' reasons on one side and 'con-Shelburne' thoughts on the other. He should then stack the items in each column in order of importance – by

> their respective weights' . . . and 'where (you) find two, one on each side, that seem equal, strike them both out and . . . find, at length, where the balance lies . . . and come to a determination accordingly.

Moral equations might do very nicely when the decision-making is individual but help not one bit in family deliberations. One can easily see the extent of confusion if a husband and wife prioritised differently, even if they could agree on all the factors relevant. Mary Priestley would likely have been very reluctant to move to the south of England, so far from her family and where she had no friends. And, migration aside, why should she share her husband with a member of the aristocracy? Priestley himself probably didn't have this perspective and was certainly attracted by the salary. At Mill Hill he was still only earning £100 a year and he was conscious of the publishing debts he had accumulated. He had already confessed to Price that he had been thinking about emigrating to America where he thought he would be able to offer Mary and the children a better lifestyle. A month on from Shelburne's visit, he was still undecided. One can sense the marital tension in the Priestley home and advice from friends, much of it unsolicited, was now arriving by each mail. Most of it was cautionary if not downright negative. Among the letters was one from Sir John Pringle that was difficult to ignore. Pringle, a royal physician and close friend of Franklin, was within weeks of his election as President of the Royal Society and was anxious lest Priestley lose his intellectual independence. On the other hand, Shelburne's face-to-face sincerity and empathy had impressed Priestley. The two men had 'conversed some hours on the subject with great frankness on both sides'. Shelburne had seen no reason why Priestley should not continue to preach whenever there was an opportunity and since he did not expect to 'engage' much of his time, that Priestley should not 'prosecute all his own pursuits with more advantage'. In particular, Priestley had been encouraged that his potential employer was able to tolerate his 'obnoxious religious sentiments' and by early November he had finally resolved to accept the position with

Shelburne. He wrote to Price that he intended to travel to London to discuss final details with him and other friends before seeing Shelburne, sharing the cost of a chaise with some other clergymen travelling south in early December. In the meantime he contacted John Lee, a barrister friend now based in London, for his legal opinion on the salary, pension and other items in the contract as he had done when there had been the possibility of sailing with James Cook.

Priestley lost no time on his arrival in London late on Sunday 6 December. He called on Lord Shelburne the next morning, taking John Lee with him. Priestley accepted the position of companion and educational adviser and agreed to base himself and his family in a house near Bowood, Shelburne's country house in Wiltshire: it was here that Shelburne's two sons were living, in the care of their great aunt, Lady Arbella Denny. Shelburne was clearly happy that his proposal was finally accepted but equally resistant to trawling through the minutiae of a contract. He would, he said, 'honour' anything within the 'outline first agreed on'. Lee was unhappy, as any lawyer would have been, that no specific terms were being tabled and said so. However, Shelburne's refusal to wade through small print prevailed and Lee was left to advise Priestley, later in the day, to write Shelburne an acceptance letter that was, effectively, a detailed contract. The proposed £250 per annum salary was, for instance, to be followed by a pension of £150 per annum if the employment ended, by disagreement or Shelburne's death, within 10 years and by a larger annuity above 10 years of employment. The phrases are resonant with legal jargon and abhorrence of ambiguity and clearly those of Lee; one can hear him dictating them. Priestley did, however, refuse to insist, as Lee had suggested, on payments in advance and apologised for Lee's professional pedantry. Shelburne replied the next morning, penning his full agreement at the foot of Priestley's letter, seemingly without any offence. Back in Leeds by Christmas, Priestley began to consider who should replace him.

To Calne 1773

HAVING ACCEPTED the position with Shelburne and having agreed to move to Wiltshire, Priestley found much to be done in the early months of 1773. He had little time for experiments and was, in any case, packing his apparatus and chemicals by mid-May. He seems to have buried bottles of the latter among the family linen for its safety admitting, later, to Mary, that the 'clothing might be a little injured'[5]. He would have been very disappointed that so much of 1773 was taken up with removals. The interruption of his scientific work came at a very frustrating time: his

CALNE STRAND ABOUT 1810 (Courtesy of Peter Treloar: Calne Town Council collection.)
This appears to be the oldest image of the centre of Calne, an engraving from the Regency period.
Though the costumes are post-eighteenth century the buildings and layout of this, the very centre of
the town, would have been those familiar to Priestley and his family.

successes had been crowned by the ultimate accolade. Just as he and his family were leaving Leeds the council of the Royal Society, under its new President, Sir John Pringle, was awarding the 39-year-old Priestley the 1773 'Copley' Gold Medal (best paper of 1772) for his submission, 'Observations on different kinds of air'. Now acknowledged as one of the best scientists in England, Priestley was having to box up all his books and apparatus and sit on his thumbs.

Priestley preached his last sermon[6] in Leeds on Sunday 16 May 1773 and arrived in Calne, with his family, sometime during the first ten days of June. At this point Joseph was 40, Mary 30 or 31 and the three children, Sally, Jos and William 10, 4 and 2 respectively. They took a room at one of the coaching inns and asked for a messenger to go up to Bowood to announce their appearance. They were soon in the presence of Daniel Bull, Lord Shelburne's Bowood agent. Bull, who had inherited the post from his father, John, in 1768, lived in Calne, at Castle House. He explained that a large family house had been rented for them. Unfortunately, some redecorations were underway and not quite finished[7]. This property has always been supposed to have been that which is now 19, The Green, so-called 'Priestley House'. Externally it has changed little since the eighteenth century. There are extensive outbuildings at the rear and the large cellars were once linked to those of the White Hart Inn[8]. A wealthy Heddington landowner, Francis Child, had refurbished the house in 1758 and lived there with his second wife Elizabeth, all of which matches the date stone on the façade[9]. Child had died, though, in 1767[10] and his family, who now actually lived elsewhere, rented out the house[11]. The current tenant was a Mr. Calley[12] but he, too, was otherwise accommodated in 1773 and the house was available for Lord Shelburne to rent for the Priestleys for the foreseeable future. Bull may have been over-optimistic in his assessment of the work still to be done on the house. It would appear, also, that he didn't reveal that the accommodation was only a rather tenuous subletting. Priestley sounded very disappointed when he wrote[13] to a friend in July:

> . . . tho' we are got into our house, we as yet occupy no more than one room in it below stairs, besides the kitchen; as something or other still remains to be done to the rest . . .

The family were having to live in such overcrowded conditions that it must have played on their nerves; boisterous children need elbow room and in new environs could not really be let out onto the streets. Priestley himself

19, THE GREEN, CALNE – 'PRIESTLEY HOUSE'
The large house on the south side of The Green, Calne, where, by tradition, the Priestley family
first lived when they arrived in Calne. It was owned by the Child family, rich landowners of
Heddington but leased to a succession of tenants in the 1770s.

was clearly at a loose end intellectually and killing time while still separated from many of his personal belongings:[14]

> My books &c are not yet arrived, but I have heard of their being safe in London, and expect them this week here; and I cannot be said to be settled till I have got these unpacked, and am got to work at my experiments, or something other.

There were other stresses, too; more serious ones. Perhaps because of all the upheaval and the inevitable exhaustion from all the responsibilities that would have fallen on her, Mary had fallen ill:[15]

> My wife has not enjoyed very good health since our arrival here. She has been troubled with an exceeding bad cough but is at present much better, and I hope will soon be quite well.

In 1773 Calne was a significant community and staging post on the London-Bath road (now the A4). There were two large coaching inns, The White Hart and The Catherine Wheel (Lansdowne Hotel). The population was about 3000[16]. The oldest and most dominant building was St. Mary's Church, little changed, in actual outline, from today. There were three Dissenter Meeting Houses and the house of a local Quaker was licensed for assemblies. Priestley found, in fact, that there was a strong thread of non-conformity in north and central Wiltshire, an area also strong in woollen manufacturing. In both these respects it must have reminded him of West Yorkshire. Calne Unitarians worshipped at a chapel on the corner of Back Road and Bollings Lane (now Linden Close). The chapel, where Priestley would have worshipped and where he preached on occasions, was destroyed in 1960 having served, late in its life, many functions including being a Salvation Army Citadel[17]. Calne's tradesmen were concentrated in Butcher's Row, the section of the London-Bath road opposite the Church but there were some shops to the north, 'beyond the bridge', in what is now the High Street, opposite the old Town Hall on Market Hill. One of the shops in Butcher's Row was a new butchery business started just three years earlier, in 1770, by a Sarah Harris from Devizes and her son John[18]. The main local industry, apart from agriculture, was the production of woollen cloth. There was a series of spinning and fulling mills along the river Marden and several of the clothiers, the woollen merchants, lived in large houses on Kingsbury (The) Green to the south of the Church. The bulk of the population was very poor, however, and lived huddled together in damp cold cottages rising from the flood plain of the River Marden. Priestley was immediately struck by the extent of the poverty in the town, describing[19] the 'poor of Calne' as 'exceedingly shabby and wretched'.

Priestley spent the summer of 1773 getting to know Lord Shelburne whose customary annual routine, typical for an aristocrat, was to spend winters (the 'season') in and around London, at Shelburne House in Berkeley Square or at his home at High Wycombe, and the summer months, June to late September, in 'the country' at Bowood. But even before Shelburne came down from London, Bull no doubt made arrangements for Priestley to attend a briefing at Bowood House. Here everything was more auspicious than in nearby Calne. The extensive construction work of the 1750s, under architect Henry Keene, had been improved and completed by Robert Adam[20.] All was now finished; the impressive buildings were pristine, the stonework gleaming, the rooms immaculate and the exquisite furnishings new. On touring the house Priestley was introduced to the staff. He met the two boys who were the main reason that Shelburne had engaged him; 7-year-old Lord John Fitzmaurice (later Lord Wycombe and second Marquis of Lansdowne) and his younger brother, the Hon. William Petty, aged 5. Priestley found Thomas Jervis already installed as the full-time tutor for the boys[21]. Jervis, born Ipswich 1748, was also a Dissenter, son of a Presbyterian Minister[22]. Like Priestley he had both attended

BOWOOD HOUSE 1806. (Courtesy of Wiltshire Heritage Museum Library, Devizes.) Drawing (original in colour) by John Buckler (1770-1851), the well-known topographical artist, in 1806. This, then, is an image of Bowood about a quarter of a century after Priestley left. However, the appearance of the house would have altered little in that time.

and taught at Dissenter Academies and been a Minister to a congregation. He had taken up his post at Bowood in 1772 (and held it until 1783). Priestley was to make conscious efforts not to 'tread on the toes' of Jervis.

It would have been quite a coincidence for Priestley to have met the 'Bowood doctor' during his first visit to the house but the two men surely met before too long. Christopher Allsup was a surgeon-apothecary (general practitioner) in Calne and 'was called in[23] to attend the family at Bowood on all occasions where medical aid was required' The orientation at Bowood perhaps ended in the library, the largest room of the new 'Diocletian' wing of the house, completed only three years before, again by Adam[24]. Here, and in the library at Shelburne House, Priestley was to spend hundreds of hours trying to organise and catalogue Shelburne's ever-growing collection of manuscripts and books, many of them antiquarian. And, next to the library, he was shown into a small room where he was invited to install, at his suggestion, equipment and apparatus such that he could demonstrate 'philosophical phenomena' to houseguests and visitors and, in time, teach the little boys. This was to be his 'elaboratory', the haven where he was to make more significant scientific discoveries.

Priestley was overjoyed to have dedicated space in which he could resume his gas experiments though he was still waiting for his books and apparatus to arrive in mid-July[25]. Having not been able to test any of his ideas for many months, his pent-up enthusiasm soon produced results, even with makeshift equipment. By the end of September he was describing, in a letter to Benjamin Franklin[26], that he had discovered another unique 'air'. Boiling 'volatile alkali', otherwise known as 'spirit of sal ammoniac' (ammonium hydroxide) gave off a vapour that could be trapped over mercury (since it was soluble in water). This gas had singular properties and Priestley called it 'alkaline air', analogous to the 'acid air' (hydrogen chloride), one of his last discoveries at Leeds. Today we call it ammonia. It was the first of several gases Priestley was to discover during his time at Bowood and Calne.

The same letter to Franklin indicates that the Priestley family accommodation constrictions had resolved, enough, certainly that he could invite the American, Franklin, to come to stay[27]. The invitation was not taken up. In fact the traffic reversed: by early November Priestley was preparing to travel to London. Being Shelburne's companion obviously meant being with him, or at least near him, throughout the year. Priestley was therefore obliged to spend the months between November and June in London. He was given a room at Shelburne House but there was no accommodation for his family who were obliged to remain in Calne. The reality of the circumstances proved traumatic. Priestley found that he hated leaving his family. His isolation from them was worse, even, than he had expected, especially when, shortly after arriving in London, he fell ill[28]. Mary, he knew to be equally miserable and lonely – she had not found any amenable company in Calne. In a letter[29] written in July 1773, only a few weeks after their arrival, Priestley had intimated, to a friend, her particular unhappiness:

. . . (my wife) is much at a loss for company of her own sex, and I do not think she is likely to be better accommodated in that respect here.

Priestley's gloomy forecast, that Mary's loneliness would not resolve, proved correct. By the time of another letter[30] to his friend William Turner at Wakefield, in February 1774, Priestley has been in London with Lord Shelburne since late November. Mary had therefore been isolated in Calne, and in the depths of winter chill and darkness, for over three months. Bar the three young children and, presumably, a servant or two hired locally, she was entirely alone. It was the first 'winter' experience of a new way of life and Mary appeared to have become rather desperate. She obviously decided to do something about her predicament and Priestley related to his friend that

my wife . . . will be with me on Monday next (21 February), and after staying for about a week, will go on to Leeds, wither I should be very happy to accompany her, but I'm afraid it will not be possible.

Mary appears to have used her brief return to the north to solve her loneliness. On her return to Calne she was accompanied by two members from her circle of friends in Leeds – the sisters Mary and Elizabeth Sewell[31]. Mary was 21 and her younger sister almost 14[32]. Priestley's reaction to having long-standing guests is unrecorded but if Mary's happiness was at stake and it made his unavoidable absences easier to bear (for both of them) he surely would have been pleased. His extended household did, however, heighten an accommodation crisis waiting for him in early summer 1774 when he returned to Calne.

In the meantime, Priestley had found that life in London had, for him, its compensations. Through Lord Shelburne he came to know many of the powerful and famous personalities of the time, names from the worlds of politics, the arts, the military and religion. He was introduced to many of them at Shelburne House, often accompanying Shelburne at table with them. And, after dinner, Shelburne would often ask him to demonstrate scientific phenomena. Priestley was able to equip a room at Shelburne House as a further laboratory, frequenting the best London instrument shops at Shelburne's expense. By May 1774 he had spent over £60 - some £4200 in present money[33]. The apparatus was used to good effect. He discovered yet another new gas – 'dephlogisticated nitrous air' (nitrous oxide). The human potential of this gas would lie dormant for some twenty years; it was Humphry Davy and his contemporaries who would discover the anaesthetic and recreational properties of the compound that came to be known as 'laughing gas'. Priestley had no 'schoolroom' responsibilities in London so he also had time to indulge in Dissenter politics, organising petitions and lobbying in Parliament. He was walking distance from the Royal Society off Fleet Street and able to attend all their meetings; the formal assemblies every Thursday and the various associated clubs and dinners. He became a regular member of the 'Club of Honest Whigs', so-named by Benjamin Franklin, another stalwart of their informal meetings at a Fleet Street coffee house.

Franklin's days in London were numbered. The impetus for independence among the American colonists was growing out of control and civil war seemed inevitable. As the most prominent American in London, Franklin was finding himself cold-shouldered. Then, in the political aftermath of the Boston Tea Party[34] and having been 'discovered' to have divulged the contents of some private letters for political advantage, he was maligned in the press as 'an old snake'[35]. Many of his close friends, even, found his presence 'inconvenient' especially after he was called to appear before The Privy Council. The hearing was in February 1774 and no Privy Council had ever been better attended. Even the Prime Minister, Lord North, turned up. Franklin was accused and personally insulted for two hours in a room in the Houses of Parliament appropriately called the Cockpit, stoically keeping a stony face under a hail of invective from Alexander Wedderburn, the Solicitor General, renowned for his bullying interrogations. Franklin's only supporter in the room was Priestley, who had managed to gain admittance in the slipstream of Edmund Burke. When the accused finally left the dock the only friendly eyes among the crowd of onlookers belonged to Priestley:[36]

> Dr. Franklin, in going out, took me by the hand, in a manner that indicated some feeling. I soon followed him, and going through the anteroom, saw Mr. Wedderburn there . . . Being known to him, he stepped forward as if to speak to me; but I turned aside, and made what haste I could out of the place.

Priestley was also with Franklin the next morning[37] to hear him predict (quite correctly) that all hopes of a reconciliation between the King and his transatlantic subjects was now lost and that he could only return to

THEOPHILUS LINDSEY (Courtesy of the Royal Society Library, London).
Portrait published by Joseph Johnson in 1809, the year after Lindsey died. Lindsey was a convert to Unitarianism and became one of Priestley's closest friends and supporters. Whenever Priestley was in London, he would always share Sunday supper with the Lindseys.

Philadelphia. After one last, ill-fated, attempt to stave off blood-loss Franklin finally set sail for America in the spring of 1775. He spent his last day in England with Priestley and, after a tearful parting[38], they never met again although they were to correspond regularly until Franklin's death in 1790.

The winter of 1773/4 also saw the culmination of a subscription and negotiations to help Priestley's other close friend, Theophilus Lindsey. He was now a renegade from the established Church and trying to establish a Unitarian chapel in central London. A disused auction house was rented, a licence obtained and the doors of the Essex Street Chapel were formally opened on 17 April 1774[39]. This place of worship, where he and Richard Price had had a major say in layout, became a second home for Priestley. From now on, whenever he was in London, he would attend Sunday evening service and then go on to have supper with the Lindseys[40].

With Lindsey safely established in his chapel, Priestley returned to Wiltshire in late April. He now learned that the house on The Green at Calne, into which he and his family had moved the previous summer, had been let to Shelburne under a very flawed agreement giving no security of tenure. Now Calley, the true tenant, was wanting to reoccupy the premises, his alternative housing arrangements having collapsed[41]. Henry Merewether, Shelburne's Steward[42] at Bowood, wrote[43] anxiously to his master on Thursday 19 May:

> Dr. Priestley has been talking very earnestly with me on the subject of his house . . . (he being) very apprehensive that there may not be another house provided in readiness for him against (the time when) . . . Mr. Calley will be obliged to occupy (it) himself . . .

Priestley, whose household had suddenly burgeoned and who had learned that Shelburne was planning to take him as companion on a tour of Europe in late summer, was understandably concerned lest his family found themselves homeless while he was so far away. But Merewether, a long-standing friend of Shelburne, had a nose for goings-on in the community and was a wise enough owl never to relate a problem without a hint at a solution:[44]

> . . . unless it be your Lordship's pleasure that the Parsonage House be purchased for him out of hand . . .

The Parsonage House is an interesting Calne property that has a long history. Significantly altered and refurbished in 1826[45], it still exists as 'The Old Vicarage' at the bottom of what is now Anchor Road (then Cow Lane). The earliest traceable record of the property is of 1699 when it was described as 'the Vicarage House'. However, it was not occupied by the Calne vicar after 1728 and was to remain in non-clerical occupancy for the next hundred years. For some of that period, ending about 1773, it was owned by a Miss Sheppard. It was always a large house, endowed with various outbuildings, in an extensive plot of land that runs around it and especially to the north-west where it is bounded by the River Marden to the west and Abberd Brook in front. Perhaps the property was too much for an ageing spinster. By 1774 it was certainly in very poor repair for, as Merewether reported to Shelburne[46], it:

> . . . will at least take up the whole of this summer to put into any habitable condition as to repairs, and which repairs indeed can be done only in the summer . . .

In the end, Shelburne did buy the Parsonage House as accommodation for Priestley and his family but the story stalls. Perhaps the expected accommodation crisis receded for a while but whatever the circumstances, the Priestley household remained at what was probably the 'Child' house on The Green until the following summer, 1775.

1774. Oxygen and Paris

IT WAS HENRY FORD who said that 'history is bunk' and at times it is certainly the case in the history of chemistry. Joseph Priestley *did not* discover oxygen. Since the one thing that most people can tell you about Priestley is that he *did* discover oxygen, this apparent nonsense needs careful explanation.

Priestley certainly discovered the gas that would, later, be called 'oxygen' The word 'oxygen' was invented by the French Chemist, Antoine Lavoisier, in 1777. In Lavoisier's concept of things it was a gas that combined with metals when they burned and the consequent 'salts' formed 'acids' with water – 'oxygine' is from the Greek; that which generates acids. Priestley's own

BOWOOD LABORATORY (Courtesy of the Trustees of the Bowood collection.). Engraving, artist unknown, of the laboratory at Bowood House as it appeared, in 1777, during its occupancy by Priestley.

name for the gas, though astutely descriptive and appropriate for the time, was an awful mouthful – 'dephlogisticated air'. He and his friends at the Royal Society had long believed the opposite to Lavoisier – that something was given up on burning. They believed in the existence of a colourless, odourless matter that was released from all substances when they were burned or rotted. This universal 'principle' was also released by breathing. It was called 'Phlogiston', 'phlox' being Greek for fire. Priestley, who, once convinced of something could rarely be dissuaded, was a fully paid-up subscriber to the Phlogiston theory; he would be so until his death, latterly in the teeth of overwhelming evidence that it was nonsense. However, in 1774, it was the best theoretical model for what happened in many chemical reactions. His discovery of 'dephlogisticated air', an air that, in his perspective, contained so little phlogiston so that it could vigorously support burning or breathing (by being able to absorb phlogiston readily) occurred, as is so typical in science, because of a coincidence of circumstances.

It was around the time of the move to Calne that Priestley, like other contemporary chemists, was having to grasp the fact that air, the substance that is all around us and which we must breathe to stay alive, was not a 'simple, elementary substance.' The scientists of the late eighteenth century began to see that they should defy their instincts and what seemed so obvious; they had to come to terms with the fact that atmospheric air was a varying mixture of several individual gases. Many of the experiments that led to this counter-intuitive insight were based on very simple methods – the techniques of so-called 'pneumatic chemistry'. In essence the 'air' being studied was collected in an inverted glass jar, the open end of which was held under water (or mercury if the particular gas dissolved in water) in a large (usually earthenware) trough. As Priestley said,[47]

> . . . we may perhaps discover principles of more extensive influence than even that of gravity itself . . . by working in a tub of water or a basin of quicksilver.

Although the basics were simple enough, Priestley and his peers were highly ingenious men. Many chemical substances were seen to fizz and bubble when heated: gases were obviously escaping, but how to heat a chemical sample that was locked inside a glass chamber? The light of the sun was called into play. If this was focussed to a point with a convex glass lens, it proved to be

BURNING LENS (Courtesy of the Library of Dickinson College, Carlisle, PA., USA.)
A 'burning lens' or 'glass' as used by Priestley in the discovery of oxygen. He used it to focus the rays of the sun onto his samples of mercuric oxide. The heat liberated a gas that he called 'dephlogisticated air': oxygen was a later name, given by the French chemist, Lavoisier.

an intense heat source (don't try this at home if you value your carpets). In fact such lenses came to be known as 'burning lenses' and Priestley now had one available at Bowood. He had bought it in London thanks to the generosity of Lord Shelburne. Some twelve inches in diameter, with a 20inch focal length and mounted in a mahogany frame[48], it had cost £6 10s. 0d. at the shop of Edward Nairne, one of the very best scientific apparatus retailers. So, in the summer of 1774, Priestley had the knowledge, the experience, the time and the equipment to perform valuable 'air' experiments. All he needed was some good fortune and this arrived in Calne during July in the person of his friend, John Warltire.

John Warltire was a curiosity of the eighteenth century, the Adam Hart-Davis of his day. He was an itinerant lecturer of science and technology. After an exotic youth in the Middle East – the son of Swiss parents – he was educated in England. He began giving lectures throughout the Midlands and West Country in 1763. He would demonstrate astronomy using his orrery, show what an air pump could do and allow audiences to peer down his microscope. He was also adept at showing experiments in electricity that were instantly entertaining. These occasions were very popular and he was able to capitalise on his success; eventually he would spend time and money on scientific experiments of his own. In July 1774 he visited Calne and stayed with Priestley. He had boxes of chemicals with him. One contained what was then known as 'mercurius calcinatus' (mercuric oxide) and he gave some to Priestley[49]. In fact, Warltire was able to

> furnish me with many substances which I could not otherwise have procured. I proceeded with great alacrity to examine, by the help of it (the burning lens), what kind of air a great variety of substances would yield.

Priestley was obviously exploring random-wise rather than following any logical plan but he soon made a remarkable discovery and it was far from luck that he had the wit to spot its significance[50].

On the 1st of August 1774 I endeavoured to extract air from mercurius calcinatus (mercuric oxide) and I presently found that, by means of this lens, air was expelled from it very readily. Having got about three or four times as much as the bulk of my materials, I admitted water to it and found that it was not imbibed by it. But what surprized me more than I can well express, was, that a candle burned in this air with a remarkably vigorous flame . . . and a piece of red-hot wood sparkled in it . . .

Hard on the heels of this tangible excitement, however, came disbelief and self-doubt. Priestley developed strong suspicions that his sample of mercuric oxide had been contaminated by 'nitre' (saltpetre, one of the components of gunpowder). Fortunately Warltire was still a guest and able to provide another sample, one he could vouch for more in terms of purity. The experiment was repeated with identical results but now there was another frustration; scientific work had to stop once more. Priestley had known since May that he was to accompany Lord Shelburne on a summer visit to the continent and the two of them left Calne for London and Dover in the third week of August.

Shelburne was an experienced traveller in Europe, having made previous trips and having served there in the British Army during the Seven Years War (1756 – 1763). He was quite at home and fluent in French. Priestley, on the other hand, was a complete novice at foreign travel. His wide-eyed astonishment at some of the everyday sights comes across in long letters[51,52,53] that he wrote to Shelburne's young sons. In many ways they made bizarre reading matter for little boys, being opinionated and parochial, but they were probably intended as open letters for everyone at Bowood to read. They serve as an interesting and unique journal, the letters he no doubt wrote to his own family having been long lost. Having travelled from Calais to Lille, Priestley reported, on 26 August, the fortifications of the towns, the ornamentation of the houses, the crudity of the furniture at the inns, and that many of the fields they had passed seemed neglected. In Lille itself, Priestley had watched, with amazement, little carts being drawn by dogs and how the local taxi-men cheated – the sedan chairs had wheels. In the meantime Lord Shelburne had been invited to inspect a regiment of French soldiers paraded in his honour. His companion didn't enjoy this at all – he was too distracted by bad toothache, the result of a sinus infection. His mood was more upbeat by the beginning of September; as his pain abated he was more positive about the prospects they watched from the carriage. He thought that the farms and fields of Austrian Flanders (Belgium) were much better tended. Other sights reminded him of his new home in Wiltshire:

> . . . in this country the boys that beg on the wayside have the very same ridiculous custom of tumbling and standing on their heads that you will see at Studley . . .

At Antwerp the travellers were reminded of the strong tradition of Flemish painting, and especially the fame of Rubens. Their local guide was in cahoots with an art 'connoisseur' who tried to sell Shelburne an 'original' canvas at a 'prodigious' price but 'milord' soon exposed him as a sharper. Another disappointment was the Belgian beer[54].

On 3 September they crossed into the United Provinces (The Netherlands) and travelled north through Rotterdam, Delft and Leyden. Some of this leg was unavoidably on water; so low-lying and wet was the land. In fact they were very conscious of the topography – all that appeared to prevent the whole of Holland from inundation by the North Sea was a narrow stretch of sand-hills that skirted the coast. Arriving in Amsterdam on 5 September, they found the harbour

> an astonishing sight. Such a number of ships is, I believe, no where else to be found in one place.

Otherwise Priestley was disparaging and they left Amsterdam earlier than intended, to travel southeast to Nijmegen and into Germany. His parting summary of the Dutch was full of waspish contempt:

> . . . the whole country of Holland does not afford any water that a man can well drink. This circumstance, at least, furnishes them with an excuse for drinking wine and spiritous liquors in great quantities, and also for smoking tobacco, with which they almost poison every body that comes near them.

Indeed, I can hardly express how very low, beastly and sordid, the manners of the common people of this country are.

The tour continued through to and up the Rhine valley and Priestley wrote more positive reports of Dusseldorf, Cologne, Bonn and Coblenz. He saw his first vineyards near the Rhine-Moselle confluence, but not, perhaps, in their full glory – there was heavy and consistent rain. The next day the sun came out and the glorious hilly countryside tempted the travellers out of their carriage – and into a misadventure:

Lord Shelburne and I, having walked before our carriage, lost ourselves, which threw me, who was the occasion of it, into great consternation. We imagined the carriage had passed us when it had not.

Saturday 17 September was a big day for Priestley. A detour was made to the village of Neider-Seltsers, the home of the famous 'Seltzer Water'. Here was one of the naturally occurring sources of the carbonated water he had discovered how to manufacture at Leeds and which so helped to make his name as a scientist (he was never to visit Pyrmont itself). By Wednesday of the following week they were climbing the very tall spire of Strasbourg cathedral having journeyed on through Mainz, Mannheim and Worms. For the next week they travelled west and after delays, when no horses could be found for the carriage, they entered Rheims.

Thursday 29 September saw them at Paris. Priestley was immediately disappointed:

In this great capital I cannot say that I was struck with any thing except the spaciousness and magnificence of the public buildings; and to balance this, I was exceedingly offended with the narrowness, dirt, and stench, of almost all the streets.

But the city was the culmination of the tour for Shelburne. He had many contacts among the 'beau monde' of the city and his daily round was a pleasant series of meals with ambassadors and aristocrats, of salons and entertainments among admiring friends, of both sexes. All this was anathema to the tight-collared Priestley and the two men appear to have led separate lives in the city after the first few days. Fortunately for Priestley, John Magellan[55] happened to be there, a good friend from London and the Royal Society. Moreover, Magellan spoke fluent French and could act as translator when he took the 'reverend doctor' to meet the Parisian 'philosophers', members of the Royal Academy of Science based at The Louvre. Here Priestley found a world in parallel to the Royal Society and much more to his taste. Even so he found it better to stick to scientific discussions and avoid religious debate. In a community that was predominantly Roman Catholic, personal offence was so easily created. He disparagingly described to Lindsey[56] the overwhelming dominance of what he called the 'wafer-God'. He was invited to dine with Antoine Lavoisier. Lavoisier, rather like Priestley, was an amateur scientist with other responsibilities – he was a tax official. Priestley, glad to have congenial company, rashly divulged, in great detail, his very recent discoveries using mercuric oxide even though he hadn't yet published them. This was to create later problems in claims to precedence but at least he was directed to a new source of the mercury compound. Everyone agreed that the purity of the chemicals produced by the Parisian pharmacist, Antoine Cadet de Vaux were unsurpassed. Mercury compounds were one of his best sellers, being prescribed widely for venereal diseases, and Priestley obtained an ounce before leaving Paris.

After more than two centuries and with no explicit indicators in any of the surviving records, there is no way of being sure why Priestley left France so abruptly and alone. It might have been the scheme all along but it does seem surprising. Such clues as we do have all hint at Priestley being unhappy in Paris. He had read in the English newspapers available there that Theophilus Lindsey, his closest friend, had broken his leg, an injury that, in those days, often led to fatal complications. This proved to be a false alarm but he certainly became introspective from having too much time on his hands:[57]

> I am quite tired of the idleness in which I spend my time here, and long exceedingly to be about my experiments, or some composition.

He was also increasingly uncomfortable with the way of life of the French upper classes[58] – 'such luxury and dissipation'. Then came the surprising news, from Westminster, that Parliament had dissolved and that there was to be a general election. Here was an excuse to bolt back to Calne. Priestley wrote to Daniel Bull that should he need help in organising the re-election of the two Calne MPs[59] then he would 'return in an instant'[60]. If Bull did reply, the letter has been lost but, whatever the pretext, Priestley left Paris long before Shelburne. He was back in London on 2 November[61] and back in Calne with his family[62] by the 5th or 6th. He certainly had a scientific motive for returning as quickly as possible. If he was to trial the mercuric oxide sample from Cadet before spring it was urgent that he get to his laboratory at Bowood before the sun finally took on its low winter orbit and failed to give enough power to his burning lens. So, by 19 November he was able to make 'very considerable progress' with further experiments[63]. The findings were the same - the observations he had made in August had not been a fluke.

Priestley returned to London 'soon after Christmas' by which time Lord Shelburne had returned from France. Both men were soon very busy: there was a new Parliament after the election and Priestley took up his experiments again. By late January he had discovered another new gas[64] – 'vitriolic acid air' (sulphur dioxide). This discovery had all the hallmarks of classic chemistry. An eclectic mixture of olive oil, mercury and 'oil of vitriol' (sulphuric acid), heated in a retort, exploded on one occasion and Priestley sustained nasty burns. The charred victim would not be deterred. He was also trying to make sense of the inconsistent, and sometimes unpredictable, results of dissolving all sorts of substances in 'spirit of nitre' (nitric acid).

Then, in early February, as the sun began to climb in the sky once more, he began to repeat, yet again, the experiments he had made with 'mercurius calcinatus' (mercuric oxide) using, this time, the burning lens at Shelburne House. The next stage in the 'discovery' of oxygen was at last under way. After a six-month delay he was beginning to see the meaning of his observations, to understand the importance of his new finding. Sometime during the first two weeks of March 1775 he began to realise that this new air was not just an uncommon gas that merely happened, by chance, to be very low in phlogiston but that it was an intensely important natural substance that could be breathed[65] – 'a most essential ingredient in the constitution of the atmosphere'. Forgetting his recent burns and ignoring all his instincts of self-preservation he collected a large jar of the gas and proceeded to breathe it through a glass tube into his mouth[66], 'gratifying' his 'curiosity'.

> The feeling of it to my lungs was not sensibly different from that of common air; but I fancied that my breath felt peculiarly light and easy for some time afterwards. Who can tell but that, in time, this pure air may become a

fashionable article in luxury. Hitherto only two mice and myself have had the privilege of breathing it.

He tried mixing it with 'nitrous air' (nitric oxide) for the first time – performing, that is, what he called his 'nitrous test' for its purity (in the sense of suitability for breathing). He found that the new gas was easily as 'pure' as common air but botched the test, not realising that he had not used enough nitrous air to complete all the possible interaction. He did notice, however, the next day, that the resultant mixture still supported a burning candle. Then, on Wednesday 8 March he watched a mouse remain perfectly comfortable in the new gas for twice the time it would have survived in ordinary air. Moreover, the air, after rescuing the mouse, still reacted and shrank with nitrous air. He saw that he needed to push his nitrous test to the limits of saturation and found, to his amazement, that five times as much nitrous air was needed as was needed to saturate common air. Here was his 'eureka' moment and on the following Wednesday, 15 March, he wrote to Sir John Pringle that he had found an air that was five to six times 'better' than common air[67]. Pringle certainly saw the significance of what was a momentous discovery and had the letter read to the Royal Society without delay - on the evening of Thursday 23 March[68]. Technically, therefore, Priestley had 'published' his discovery of oxygen and might have been forgiven for wallowing in some justified self-satisfaction. Unfortunately, as we shall see, he had no time for celebrations and he was in considerable pain with a crop of boils. Further details of his major discovery were released, haphazardly, in further letters to the Royal Society[69]. Encouraged by Pringle, Priestley went on to adapt the contents of these three letters into a formal paper - 'An account of further discoveries in air' – that the Royal Society published in their Transactions of 1775[70] and he published in book form[71] early the next year.

It is true to say, then, that Priestley took three bites at the 'oxygen' cherry. In 1772 he had produced the gas without sensing its existence (missed a discovery); in 1774 he isolated it repeatedly but failed to see its significance (made a discovery); and, finally, in early 1775 he both isolated it, analysed it, and understood it to be a unique chemical element (discovered what he'd discovered).

The protracted and almost chaotic way in which Priestley's most famous scientific discovery was made and published has long given historians of science issues to debate. Was Priestley really the first to discover oxygen or did claims from among French 'philosophers', that they knew of the gas before Priestley told them how to make it in October 1774, have validity? Priestley was always adamant that Lavoisier and his friends had only learned of the gas from him and always regretted his candour in Paris. But Priestley and Lavoisier were not the only finalists in this competition. A Swedish apothecary/chemist called Carl Scheele describes in his book[72] how he, too, had discovered what he called 'fire air'. He always claimed that his discovery had been in 1771 but he didn't publish his book until 1777. And so, in the nature of these things, Priestley could claim precedence: he had manufactured oxygen totally independently, had eventually understood his discovery for what it was, and had been the first to publish. Even so we must remind ourselves that Priestley's obduracy tarnished the lustre of his genius. He was to go to his grave as a 'phlogistonist', having taken, therefore, his very last breath of 'dephlogisticated air'. For the man who had discovered the gas, the term 'oxygen' always remained a heresy.

1775. Calne and London

THROUGHOUT THE SPRING OF 1775, during the rather stumbling revelations and impromptu publications on oxygen, there were two subplots in Priestley's life; circumstances that would suddenly require him at home in Calne. This explains, perhaps, why he felt obliged to leave London hurriedly in the days immediately after his seminal oxygen 'breakthrough' and why he was not at the Royal Society to hear its reading and bask in the approbation of the fellows. His need to be back in Calne may also explain why he chose to travel while he was ill – he still had very painful boils. The problems he found in Calne were domestic. The insecurity of the Priestley accommodation was once again acute and there was another crisis behind the rather cryptic comment to his friend Lindsey in his first letter[73] back to London on Wednesday 15 March:

> I am at length, I thank God, got home well and find my family well. The girl was fully acquitted, and the young man will marry her.

Parish records, certainly those of the eighteenth century, have to be interpreted warily but they do, sometimes, tell a story unambiguously. The marriage register of St. Mary's Church Calne for 1775[74] shows that a Mary Sewell married a Joseph Perkins, baker, on Sunday 16 April. Sewell is not a name that appears anywhere in Calne parish records before this date. It is possible to surmise, therefore, that Mary, the older of the two young friends that Mary Priestley had brought down from Leeds, in 1774, to keep her company when her husband was away[75] had developed a relationship with Perkins. And there is a very strong hint, in being 'acquitted' by a promise of marriage, that she was pregnant. Confirmation of this interpretation of circumstantial evidence might be expected from searching the Calne baptism records. However, there appears to be no such clinching entry. Of course, if there had been a pregnancy, there might equally have been a miscarriage or a stillbirth. Or, if the young couple were Dissenters there may not have been a formal baptism. The newly married couple could have moved away from Calne: but they hadn't. They are recorded[76] as the parents of a child, Thomas, born on 6 March 1777 and baptised at St. Mary's Calne on 8 June. Sunday 8 June 1777 was a big day for these young parents but more important than might be expected: they took *two* children to the church for baptism[77]. They also presented James, born, they said, on 12 November 1775. This may have been the true date of birth but by eighteen months it is difficult to age a child precisely. Assuming James had been born at full term in November 1775, he would have been conceived in mid-February. In which case Mary could not have recognised her pregnancy until well into April – after Priestley's panicky return from London and his letter to Lindsey. Was there, then, some leeway around the quoted date of birth of James, a licence that was possible at a delayed baptism? We shall probably never know. However, the elements of this story all make sense if Mary Sewell had conceived in December or January 1774/5 and had been delivered of her first baby, James, as Mrs Mary Perkins, around September 1775, six months after her marriage. In which case she would have been confessing her predicament to a horrified Mary Priestley in March 1775. One can imagine the urgency with which a Minister's wife would write to her husband. Oxygen was not the only discovery Priestley made that month.

Then there was the accommodation crisis in Calne. This time it would not go away but thankfully Lord Shelburne had picked up on the hint from Merewether, his Steward, and had bought[78] the Parsonage House. The property was not a good buy and was to cost him a lot of money. As the weather improved during spring and early summer 1775 the craftsmen and labourers descended on the house. Merewether had been right; there was much to do to put it into a 'habitable condition'[79]. The invoices for the work done, which accumulated at Bowood between May and Christmas that year, are signal evidence[80] to the investment needed. Replacing the roof timbers (Thomas Bridgman, sawyer and Charles Oakford, carpenter) and putting back all the tiles (Henry Ashford), together with making good all the loose and missing plaster cost almost £200. It looks as though many, if not all, of the windows were replaced for Robert Freshwater, glazier, was paid £36 11s. 5d. Work[81] by John Button, mason, cost £21 10s. and that of Edward Eatwell, blacksmith, £10 5s. 3d. One would expect other bills, from painters and decorators for instance, but the next relevant accounts book is missing. The last entry in the one for 1764 – 1776[82] is particularly interesting, however. The invoice is worth quoting verbatim:

> Paid Labourers for levelling Ground and sinking the Fish Pond at the Parsonage House on by note of Particulars £23 14s. 11d.

Here, surely, is 'Doctor's Pond' and the answer to a present-day conundrum. When visitors go to the low-lying area of Calne where Abberd Brook runs into the Marden, in the northeast corner of Somerfield's car park, they find a Calne Civic Society blue plaque announcing 'Doctor's Pond'. They look for the pond in vain be they residents or tourists. It no longer exists even though its location is confidently given as nearby, presumably by word of mouth evidence over generations. The only three bodies

THE PARSONAGE HOUSE, CALNE (now The Old Vicarage) where the Priestley family lived 1775-1780. The older part of the house (which was extensively refurbished in the early nineteenth century) can be seen to the right of the front door.

of water are the River Marden, Abberd Brook, and a pond some 150 yards upstream alongside the Abberd watercourse. The latter is a red herring. It was cut out in the 1950s but is a useful illustration of how a pond within the land abutting the Parsonage House (the paddock) would have been filled by a leat from the brook. In 1775 the average labourer's wage was about 8 pence a day[83]. The cost of digging out the pond (assuming it to have been about half of the cost of all the ground works quoted) was equivalent, therefore, to some 355 days of labour – say 16 men for three weeks. 'Doctor's pond' must have been a substantial feature of the land belonging to the Parsonage House and, in order to fill it, it must have been in the lowest part of the land to the north (front) of The Parsonage House. We have no evidence of when it was filled in.

The Priestleys moved into the Parsonage House early in July 1775 – before it was finished. Once again they had to suffer the disruption of tradesmen still being present in the property:[84]

At present we are in a good deal of confusion, having the carpenters below stairs while we live above.

Nevertheless Priestley himself was very pleased with the house[85]:

I am just got into my house in Calne, and, upon the whole, like the situation very well.

So he should have done; it was going to be an impressive and comfortable home. We have the good fortune to know many details of the accommodation because John Cross (Bowood agent) and William Essington (Merewether's replacement as Shelburne's Steward) later took upon themselves, as good estate management practice, to detail a valuation[86] of all fixtures and fittings in all the rooms. Thus we learn that the house had a parlour, a best parlour, a kitchen, a pantry, a storeroom, a back kitchen and laundry, a cellar and five bedrooms. It also had a laboratory. So, Priestley now had three laboratories, one at home, one at Bowood and one at Shelburne House. It's ironic, therefore, that as his facilities for experimenting peaked, his output as a scientist diminished – his most productive years as a pioneer in gas chemistry were over. After 1775 his discoveries were few and very much a footnote.

Expected in London for the winter 'season', Priestley left Calne for Shelburne House once more[87] on Monday 23 October 1775. It gave him a few days to resettle himself in the capital and bring his laboratory back to life. These were necessary preparations and rehearsals for Lord Shelburne had invited, for early November, a party of dignitaries, a Russian delegation among them, to watch Priestley demonstrate some of his experiments[88]. Not that Priestley would have allowed this commitment to prevent him visiting Johnson, his publisher, in the Strand. The manuscript[89] of 'Airs II' had been sent on 7 July and it was high time to check on its passage through the presses. In fact Johnson had made reasonable progress and the unstitched pages were all ready by early December. The details of the discovery of 'dephlogisticated air' (oxygen) were about to be made available to the general public. Then it was back to the familiar routine of writing, experimenting, attending Royal Society meetings, chapel and the Lindseys on Sundays, arguing with fellow philosophers in the coffee houses and chewing on Dissenter politics. How much he still attended on Lord Shelburne, dining, accompanying and advising – his day job after all – is not clear but the stressful distance from his family was still an issue – at Christmas he raced back to Calne[90].

1776. Calne and London

A LTHOUGH NOT COMPLETELY WELL, Priestley saw it his duty to return to London on Saturday 6 January 1776[91]. An unpleasant, cold journey reflected the pangs, yet again, of separation from his family. On the other hand he expected Johnson to be stacking stitched copies of his second volume on 'Airs' by now and he was planning some experiments to show how blood passing through the lungs discharges phlogiston (absorbs oxygen in modern understanding). A few trips to the slaughterhouses in west London provided him with enough gruesome material to prove his theory and by mid-February he was writing[92] excitedly to Franklin at Philadelphia. The letter was enclosed in a parcel containing one of the first copies of 'Airs II' and entrusted to a Major Carleton, brother of the Governor of Quebec. Carleton was about to leave for America. There was some risk of the package never reaching Philadelphia, of course, but Priestley seemed very cavalier towards a more serious outcome: if the letter had fallen into the wrong hands its contents could have had him arraigned for treason:

> When Lord Germaine[93] is at the head of affairs, it cannot be expected that anything like reason or moderation should be attended to . . . everything breathes rancour and desperation . . . we therefore look upon a final separation from you as a certain and speedy event (and that) you will be driven to the necessity of governing yourselves.

In typically reckless manner[94] he also sent Franklin, now one of the enemy, Lord Shelburne's 'best respects and good wishes'. In fact Priestley was becoming very involved in the policy debates around the American crisis and sat up until one o'clock one morning[95] to read a pamphlet by Dr. Price.

He also attended[96], with Lindsey, a House of Lords debate on 14 March. But there was also personal news for Franklin. By the time he penned the letter, Priestley had also been to visit the American's ex-landlady and close friend, Margaret Stephenson[97] at 36, Craven Street[98], off the Strand. 'Mrs. S' was 'much as usual' and could 'talk about nothing but you'. Franklin's old servant, Le Fevre, was also nostalgic about his erstwhile master. And to keep the warm glow alight, Priestley reminded Franklin how much he was missed by the 'club of honest Whigs'. Priestley's last surviving letter from London in the spring of 1776 was dated 25 April[99]. It was to Volta, thanking him for the details of his new discovery, the 'electrophore'. The Turin professor had discovered a way of electrifying a cake of hard resin such that it stored the charge; it was the genesis of what we now know as the battery.

In Calne, all seemed well at The Parsonage House and Mary's strawberry plants were already bearing fruit[100]. Priestley did find, though, two items of relevant news at Bowood. Lord Shelburne was planning a further continental trip but did not expect Priestley to accompany him this time. Whether or not this was because Priestley would be needed at Bowood is not clear. However, a commitment 'at home' might have been used diplomatically, and there was one. Thomas Jervis would be away for at least a month, visiting friends during a well-earned break[101] and Priestley would be needed in the schoolroom. He seemed to express no regrets about missing out on further foreign travel. Rather, he grieved[102] over the loss of long summer days that he might otherwise have dedicated to science:

> While I am doing Mr. Jervis's duty at Bowood, I shall be under the necessity of suspending my experiments.

Diverted from the laboratory, Priestley took up theological issues again. He managed to finish his Greek Harmony – a long essay, in Greek, in which he attempted to explain away the discrepancies between the four Gospels by using the earliest and least adulterated texts. A version in English was to follow, three years later. There was nothing controversial about this theological sudoku but from now on he seemed to abandon the diplomatic reticence in religious matters that he had adopted when taking up the post with Shelburne. He had published only three theological tracts since 1771 but now he began to pen some very contentious personal beliefs, invoking the thoughts and theories of other thinkers in some very eccentric ways that they would find insulting. His trenchancy seemed to blind him from any sense of tact or ability to see the delicacy of his position with Shelburne.

In late August 1776 Lord Shelburne left on his trip to Europe[103]. The fact that Priestley did not go with him marked a significant change in their relationship. The companionship mandate of Priestley's role was clearly not working. Taking each year in their relationship to have lasted from one June to the next, the two men had spent at least five months in each other's close company in 1773/4, 1774/5 and 1775/6. But from late 1776 they subsequently never spent more than a month or two together, at the most. Priestley was ensconced more and more with Mary and the children at Calne. 1776 can be seen as the beginning of the end.

Priestley could never stay away from his experiments for very long. The citizens of Calne, going about their daily business, couldn't help remarking on the sight of the 'Doctor', in his dark silks, squelching about in the boggy boundary of his pond or in Abberd marsh. Just what he was doing poking and prodding in the shallow water and holding bottles under the surface was a matter of mystery to them. He was actually collecting 'inflammatory air' (methane). It was certainly a good time to be working on this gas - its source is, after all, rotting vegetation and the pond at The Parsonage House was still only a year old, its clay base still frothing. But in the community there was a currency of wild conjecture on street corners and smirking in the alehouses; ignorant theories abounded about 'Doctor's pond'. It's easy to see how, over the generations, the myth grew that it was here that he had discovered oxygen; after all 'bog-bottling' was the one aspect of all his regular activities that was played out in public.

Priestley clearly enjoyed the privilege of the free time he now had but appeared to be resigned to the fact that his future employment by Shelburne was going to be different if not abbreviated. He was almost fatalistic:[104]

> It often gives me concern that I am so little use to your Lordship; but I flatter myself I shall be of more use to your Lordship's children, and that if, by your Lordship's generous encouragement, I be of use in promoting useful science, and rational knowledge of other kinds, your Lordship will not think your patronage be ill bestowed.

Clearly his role as an adviser on education would fizzle out anyway as the Shelburne boys matured and Priestley seemed to sense that patronage alone was not likely to support the status quo now that it was obvious that the 'companionship' mandate had not worked. Perhaps he felt, deep down, that he had nothing to lose by returning to contentious theological writings. A new manuscript[105] – a reversion to religious polemics - that Johnson printed and put on sale in 1777 as 'Disquisitions on Matter and Spirit' would bring Priestley a great deal of trouble, not least with Shelburne himself. 'The past is a different place, they do things differently there'[106] certainly applies to theology. It is very difficult, now, to understand many of the dogmatic differences in belief that so 'charged up' theologians of the eighteenth century. The enlightenment, the growing influence of science and technology, was changing the agenda: 'reason' was challenging 'revelation'. Priestley straddled both of these domains and tried to live in both camps. Central to his 'Disquisitions' was his attempt[107] to 'prove that man has no soul besides his brain'. He was encouraged that some close friends, Lindsey among them,[108] agreed with his reasoning but many were frankly appalled by the inevitable implications. A large number, including Richard Price, were repelled by Priestley's proposal that, on death, the soul died with the body – both being only 'matter', after all. This was called 'materialism' and was much derided: many saw it as atheism. According to Priestley, there would be, one distant day, a universal resurrection of all former life but in the meantime there was no surviving soul to rise to heaven (or sink into hell). This huge challenge to the doctrinal conventions of the older 'established' churches and of the majority of Dissenters was going to create a storm. Initially there was some light relief; a fellow Welsh Dissenting Minister sent Richard Price a witty ditty[109] that was soon in common circulation:

> Here I lie at rest,
> In oaken chest,
> Together packed most nicely,
> The bones and brains,
> Flesh blood and veins,
> And *soul* of Dr. Priestley.

But Priestley had gone further. Having met, at Paris, another 'scientific divine', Abbé Roger Boscovich[110], he was familiar with this philosopher's theory of matter. Boscovich had taken the Newtonian concepts of planetary interactions – their forces of attraction and repulsion - into the realms of the infinitesimal. He had proposed that all matter consisted simply of infinitely small identical 'atoms', only their relative interacting strengths of attraction and repulsion giving different materials their characteristics. Priestley used this precocious theory to support his version of 'materialism' and, by default, Father Boscovich, a devout Catholic who drew a very clear line between his religion and his philosophical ponderings after having had to leave Milan under a doctrinal cloud, become part of this revolutionary canon. The phrase 'light blue touch paper and retire' could have been a personal motto for Priestley.

In the meantime, Priestley was still responsible to Lord Shelburne and there were more mundane issues at hand. Lord Fitzmaurice had a summer eye infection and although Dr. Allsup's treatment had helped, Priestley wrote a report[111] to Shelburne, now at Paris, that it was 'much better than it had been' though 'still causing concern'. Then there was the ongoing task of making sense of the books and documents that Shelburne had allowed to accumulate at Bowood. Priestley seemed to find this a tiresome chore, bleating[112] that his efforts would 'answer no purpose' until the bookcases were all installed. His own papers appear to have been in better order. These now included the manuscript pages of what would become his third volume on 'Airs', published in 1777[113]. Priestley spent the whole of the autumn of 1776 in Calne, feverishly finishing the work and polishing off his 'Disquisitions'. From 31 October there was an exploration at Silbury Hill[114] where the Duke of Northumberland was involved. The vertical shaft, from the top, was actually dug by Mendip miners under a Colonel Drax from Bath. It's very difficult to believe that Priestley did not visit the site if only to be able to report to Lord Shelburne and Priestley knew the Duke personally, as we have seen. Then, both Shelburne and Priestley were subscribers[115] when the new Bath Agricultural Society (now the Bath and West Society) was inaugurated in September 1777, as was Edward Drax.

He went up to London only towards the end of January 1777. He may have intended to return to the capital earlier but there were problems at Calne Unitarian Chapel. Mr. Williams, the Minister, was 'lost' during November[116] It is not known whether he had died or resigned but clearly Priestley became very involved in finding a replacement and probably filled the breach on several Sundays either side of Christmas.

1777. Calne and London

ALTHOUGH PRIESTLEY was obligated to return to Shelburne House in early 1777, he might have preferred not to have gone up to London at all for Mary was now five months into her fourth pregnancy. In the end he left Calne near the end of January. He certainly waited until his two sons were settled back at school in Devizes[117] begging use of a small carriage from the Bowood mews to take them there on 21 January.[118] Shortly after arriving in London he received a letter from Franklin but was very surprised to find that his great friend was no longer in America, at Philadelphia, but in Paris. Franklin had sailed back to Europe, arriving off the coast of Brittany in December 1776 – 'an old man in a small boat'[119]. He had been sent, by the Congress, to raise support, financial and military, in France. The mission was certainly full of uncertainty but also ironic – a neonate republic getting into bed with one of the oldest monarchies known. The Americans reckoned, though, that France would do almost anything to antagonise England and they were right. It was only a few months before a state of war spanned the English Channel, not that Priestley allowed this to get in the way of a long friendship and continued corresponding with Franklin via travellers, even sending parcels of books in defiance of discretion.

By 11 March, barely a month after arriving 'in town', Priestley was already telling friends that he was soon going back to Calne[120]. Mary was 'in indifferent spirits' and her labour imminent. Priestley was home by Easter and a further son, Henry (Harry), was born on 24 May. He was named in honour of Lord Shelburne (Henry being one of the traditional names of the Shelburne family) and seemingly at Shelburne's instigation[121]. For a while there was much to buoy up the atmosphere in The Parsonage House and Priestley appears to have combined his paternal duties with clearing a backlog of correspondence. He wasn't totally housebound however, and reported[122] to

Volta that he had much enjoyed repeating the Italian's experiments on 'inflammatory air' (methane). If Priestley's mudlarking set tongues wagging and his theological musings were those of an apparent madcap, some of his domestic behaviour was just as eccentric. In early June, as soon as Mary was back on her feet, he presented her with a pigeon for the kitchen[123]. It featured on the dinner table a day or two later. At what stage, exactly, in this culinary adventure, he told Mary and Sally that he had kept it 'sweet' for over six weeks by sealing it up in 'nitrous air' is not clear.

Later in the summer of 1777, during a period that seemed very settled and domesticated, Priestley had time for many new gas experiments but found himself drawn into more and more research which he described[124] as 'general chemistry'. This created a need for new apparatus and more chemicals, neither of which he could afford. John Warltire paid another visit in October and may have gifted some of the chemicals but Priestley played out an ulterior ruse in the hope of gaining access to new equipment. He organised for his friend to give some demonstrations at Bowood[125]. Lord Shelburne himself was away but received a forthright report[126] from his younger son, William:

> Mr. Bull and Mrs. Priestley came to see a lecture on the solar microscope, by Mr. Waltire, which lasted for 2 hours, and the same gentleman entertained us today with a very curious Lecture upon the Eye.

Priestley was probably hoping that Lord Shelburne would be moved to tolerate yet more money being spent on scientific apparatus. He sought justification in suggesting that Shelburne's older son, at least, was now reaching an age, and a stage in his education, where he would benefit from studying 'natural philosophy'. There are indications of a growing resistance, however. Priestley felt the need to preface his aspirations[127] with the remark 'when your Lordship shall be rich . . .'. Priestley's ploy might have worked but his published theological musings were about to backfire. In the meantime he appears not to have travelled up to Shelburne House that autumn, remaining in Calne for the rest of the year.

1778. Calne

THE YEAR 1778 begins with a desperate tragedy at Bowood. Some of the details are known to us from the reliable account[128] given by Mr. Jervis when a very old man in 1831. That January, routine at Bowood was as usual. Lord Shelburne was in London attending to political matters and his two sons were having classes with Jervis studying, among other topics, the letters of Cicero. It was the daily custom to break off from the books around midday and 'ride out' for exercise. One morning the prospects from the saddle were especially attractive – the day was 'frosty, but under the influence of a clear sky and bright sun.' Well-wrapped against the cold, the two boys, accompanied by Jervis and a groom, enjoyed their ride and the ten-year old William was particularly animated and cheerful at dinner[129]. Late that evening, however, he complained, to his servant, of severe abdominal pains. Dr. Allsup was sent for. He visited immediately but could find no cause for real alarm. He administered 'some medicine' (no doubt a purgative). The boy's symptoms eased and the house settled down for the night. The next day,

JOSEPH PRIESTLEY IN MIDDLE AGE (Courtesy of the Royal Society Library, London). The origin of this image of Priestley is obscure. It appeared as frontispiece to a book entitled 'The life of Joseph Priestley LLD, FRS' by John Corry, published in 1804 (the year of Priestley's death) by Wilks and Grafton, Birmingham. It appears to be Priestley in middle age and corroborates the features seen in other portraits (compare with that on the front cover and with the frontispiece).

however, the patient was obviously still in distress from time to time. Only towards evening, though, did his condition cause real concern as he became faint and delirious. A messenger was sent down to Calne to fetch back Dr. Allsup urgently. Allsup hurried to Bowood but, to his horror, all was 'distress and confusion' when he reached the portico: William had died a few minutes earlier. It was Jervis's unenviable task to take an express coach to London the next day in order to break the terrible news to the boy's father. Shelburne's devastation and grief comes down the centuries through Jervis's pained description. Priestley had not been at Bowood through all these terrible events although he was still in Calne. When he returned to London in February he must have spent the whole journey wondering what he might best say to console Lord Shelburne. In the meantime the dead boy was taken for burial in the family vault under the church at High Wycombe, to lie near his mother.

Now was hardly the time to push his luck with Shelburne's generosity but Priestley still headed for the glassware and instrument shops and bills[130] arrived at Shelburne House amounting to £165 (nearly £10,000 in present money). Priestley also chose this very difficult time for Shelburne to throw another antagonistic squib. Despite his satellite status and his supposed supportive role as an adviser he decided to voice his strong personal support for American independence in a letter to his employer, proposing that:

> . . . we have the true magnanimity and wisdom to join with France in acknowledging the independence of America..

This was contrary to Shelburne's own political stance, one he had just declared in a speech in the House of Lords, as Priestley well knew. Unusually for Priestley, the gist of his rebellion was wrapped up in a poultice of apology: but as a 'proof of a perfect attachment', the letter[131] to Shelburne on 20 March was totally disingenuous – the antagonism was absolutely explicit. Shelburne didn't respond in kind as far as one can tell but there might well have been some tense conversations. It was another crack in the breaking shell of their relationship.

By April Priestley was back in Calne and beginning a new series of experiments, exploring the behaviour of plants trapped under water[132]. Not surprisingly he had most success with aquatic plants and took native species from Calne streams and ponds. He admitted to having no botanical knowledge and could not name many of them[133]. The plants all appeared to give off bubbles of air that could be collected and tested. His analyses were inconsistent, however, and he was confused; sometimes the plants released dephlogisticated air (air rich in oxygen), sometimes it was vitiated or phlogisticated air (rich in carbon dioxide). He assumed that the differences related to the health and growth rates of the plants, expressing his thinking in a letter[134] to Landriani. The letter was dated from Milford On Sea, which signified an unexpected change in routine. It had become the custom for Jervis and some of the other Bowood staff to take Lord Shelburne's sons to the coast for a few weeks every summer. 1778 was no exception bar the facts that Lord Fitzmaurice would have been pining for his younger brother and that Jervis cried off. Priestley went in his place but obviously treated it as a working holiday; the never-ending traffic of documents and proofs between him and Johnson, his printer in London, were simply diverted to the small seaside town on the Solent.

On his return to Calne he was asked to wait on Lord Shelburne urgently. Trouble had been brewing in his absence. Priestley feared that his employer was about to protest that he has been extravagant in buying scientific apparatus and all the way up to Bowood he probably rehearsed his mantra[135] – that the best-equipped laboratory was the best environment for Lord Fitzmaurice to be inspired into studying 'philosophy' Actually his assumption was wrong. Shelburne was certainly aggrieved[136] but his first gripe was that Priestley has been abusing the privilege of corresponding at his expense – using Shelburne's postal 'covers' to have substantial parcels of books delivered from his printer. A considerable bill had been pointed out to Shelburne. But there was worse, far worse. During Priestley's vacation at Milford, Shelburne had received a fuming letter from an old French acquaintance, Father Roger Boscovich. Priestley also knew Boscovich and could guess, immediately, the reason for Shelburne's obvious displeasure. Boscovich was incensed that Priestley had used his theory of the structure of matter to support the controversial view, in 'Disquisitions', that man did not have a soul; that on death all the 'atoms' decayed until such time that there would be a universal resurrection. Souls, to paraphrase Priestley, did not exist outside a body and did not make their way to heaven, or to hell. This, of course, was anathema to a devout Catholic. Priestley's own prediction that his views would shock and offend had come true although, typically, he had applied a positive gloss. He wrote to a friend[137] that there had been 'much less alarm than was generally expected' Not that there was an under-reaction at Bowood: Shelburne had every right to be annoyed. He was now involved in Priestley's latest religious heresy and mud sticks: as a Whig he believed in religious toleration but was not an atheist and didn't relish the epithet. Boscovich was rightly demanding a wholesale retreat and a public retraction. When Shelburne handed over the actual letter Priestley found it to be in French but was able to feel, immediately, the heat in phrases such as 'abominable, detestable and impious calumny; attacking my religion, probity and honour'[138]. An apology seemed so appropriate that Shelburne probably assumed that an olive branch was inevitable and hoped the controversy would die down. If so he was wrong. Grovelling was not Priestley's way. Already in a hole, he just kept digging. Far from backing down, Priestley complained to Boscovich of the 'injury' that he had done him in writing to his patron; that it could have caused an 'irreparable and fatal' rift between them. It was as if he were trying to blame someone else for what was already happening. With a fanaticism that verged on madness he then proceeded to describe the Church of Rome in highly inflammatory terms – it was a 'corrupted' version of Christianity, 'a system of abomination little better than heathenism' and the home of the 'Antichrist'. And as if to prove that he had completely cut the ties to reality, he ended by demanding that Boscovich wrote Shelburne a retraction – another letter 'in a strain somewhat different from your last'.

At least Priestley retreated on the postage front. Phrases such as 'direct to me under cover to Lord Shelburne' that had ended many of his previous private letters subsequently disappeared. The expected 'discussion' with Shelburne on the expenses related to superfluous scientific equipment was not long delayed. For three years Priestley had been equipping three laboratories – at Bowood House and at Shelburne House but he now had, also, a well-equipped outbuilding at the Parsonage House[139]. The latter could hardly be hidden behind the smokescreen of Lord Fitzmaurice's education but this didn't seem to inhibit his shopping. In 1778 bills came in for some £275[140] (equivalent, now, to some £17,000) not counting one for Bristol glass. Shelburne probably put a stop to all this expenditure. There are no similar invoices whatsoever among later Bowood accounts, a somewhat selective absence if they have simply gone missing. There is also evidence from the fact that Priestley subsequently hinted to friends in London that he might now need financial support in order to continue his experiments. In fact the response, a subscription[141] organised by Dr. Fothergill[142], was so positive that he was forced to refuse the bulk of the money lest Lord Shelburne 'takes umbrage'[143].

1779. *Calne*

PRIESTLEY APPEARS to have been in Calne for the whole of the summer and autumn of 1778. He was able to be with his family for another Christmas and New Year and only returned to London after 6 January 1779[144]. He was bearing the burden of a problem. There was a crisis in the family finances despite the 1770s being a time of low inflation. The causes were personal and pressed in during his loneliness at Shelburne House. Priestley's own home and his family were now larger and the very significant sums of Lord Shelburne's money that had subsidised his experiments and his publishing looked to have dried up. Priestley already knew that Fothergill and friends were willing to support his scientific activities but there was no alternative source of income for family expenses. Priestley waited for an auspicious moment to approach Lord Shelburne for an increase in his salary. Despite all the recent setbacks in their relationship, Shelburne agreed[145] a generous raise – a 'very obliging and liberal proposal'. But the response to this news from the Parsonage House was a fierce and frigid letter from Mary. Having failed to discuss things with her before broaching Shelburne, Priestley read that his wife was very antagonistic. He was obliged to eat dust and tell Shelburne (in a note[146]) that Mary was

> . . . much concerned that I should have troubled your Lordship on the subject. She very much prefers continuing just as we are, rather than attempt any improvement in our circumstances, either at Calne or any other place, and will endeavour by a more rigid economy, to bring our expenses within our income.

Mary didn't want to be even more obligated to Shelburne and knew that Priestley would earn much less in any other position, not more. They should be preparing for a loss of income, not enjoying a higher one; the family must economise. Note, also, the clear hint that Mary, too, already sensed that Priestley's employment with Shelburne was doomed.

Spring 1779 was a particularly beautiful one after a mild winter and a very dry period up to Easter[147]. Priestley was more elated than usual by the journey back to Calne in late May and, as if inspired by the verdancy, again spent the summer months experimenting with plants. He was again focussed, as were others that year, on the gases released by vegetation when it was trapped under water and the fundamental question of how the atmosphere is 'purified'. He began by using willow and duckweed pulled from Abberd Marsh, taking time there to collect more 'inflammatory air' (methane) from the mud[148] He had also become very interested in the 'green matter', the algal growth we all associate with stagnant water although he was unsure, at this point, that it was living material at all[149]. By August he was trying to work out the interplay between light, warmth and growth on his plants' ability to release air bubbles under water but the weather broke:[150]

> . . . tho' of late he (the sun) has not minded his business so closely as I wished him to have done.

The clue that light was a major influence on gas exchange in plants had come from London, from his old friend John Magellan who was inside the (supposedly confidential) circle of Dr. Jan Ingen Housz[151]. Ingen Housz, on leave from his position as Royal Physician to the Imperial Court at Vienna in order to give the annual invitation lecture (Bakerian) to the Royal Society in June, had then secreted himself in the countryside near London. By mid-July he had shown that plants released oxygen very readily; but only in sunlight[152]. This was the beginning of our modern understanding of photosynthesis and a head start in the race to unravel one of nature's biggest secrets.

The laboratory was not all of Priestley's life, however. In early July he had travelled to Exeter with Thomas Jervis. The latter's younger brother, John, was being ordained and Priestley gave the sermon at the service[153] – on the parable of the sower He then spent a few days with his friend, the Revd. Joseph Bretland before returning to be at home to host a 10-day stay of other friends – the Revd. Radcliffe Scholefield and his sister[154]. The Scholefields were from Birmingham, a fact that would soon be very significant.

Lord Shelburne also had a busy summer. In 1778 he had been engaged to be married to a Miss Molesworth[155] but the young lady in question had broken off the arrangement. There had been emotional scenes at the dinner table shortly before the planned wedding but Shelburne eventually took this disappointment with good grace. Then, in late 1778 or early 1779 he began a relationship with Lady Louisa Fitzpatrick and this time there was no false start. The couple married on Tuesday 13 July 1779. The union gave Shelburne new connections and yet more prominence in the political world. Lady Louisa was sister to The Earl of Upper Ossory and to Richard Fitzpatrick, a politician close to Charles James Fox and the Holland family. Though long seen as a lieutenant of Lord Chatham (Pitt the Elder), this powerful statesman had died in May 1778 and Shelburne was coming to be seen as the leader of an important circle of opposition Whigs. He was having to take more care that his personal and social contacts were 'acceptable' to his followers; an articulate and hot-blooded Dissenter was now an embarrassment. In the meantime Priestley himself became, to use his own words, 'a widower'[156]. Mary and Sally left Calne in September and returned to Leeds with baby Henry in arms. It appears that Mary had finally had enough of her life in Calne and she never really returned (perhaps only to pack the family belongings about a year later). Priestley himself remained, nominally, at least, still working for Lord Shelburne, and the two older boys remained at school in Devizes.

In the middle of the third week of October, Priestley and Allsup were notified[157], from Bowood, that Dr. Ingen Housz was expected. Ingen Housz was on his way to Bath, to visit Sir John Pringle, his patron[158]. Pringle had resigned his presidency of the Royal Society, partly because of a conflict with the King on the best shape for lightning conductors; but he was also ill and was now 'taking the waters'. It was the last time that Pringle and Ingen Housz were to enjoy each other's company[159]. Ingen Housz was at Bowood on Friday and Saturday 15/16 October, accepting a long-standing invitation from Lord Shelburne whom he had known for nearly a decade[160]. The Royal Physician was full of the news of his summer experiments on plants and was bearing copies of his freshly printed book[161]. There were presentation copies all round and the company discussed the contents with the author. Shelburne and Allsup, who both now knew Priestley well, probably sensed that the congratulations being offered by Priestley were bogus. The previously unchallenged champion of the chemistry of gases now knew that the breakthrough in the understanding of plants, light and oxygen had been made by a competitor: he himself had failed to see the primacy and power of sunlight and was no longer top of the podium. Ingen Housz went on his way bearing memorable first impressions of 'Beauwood'[162] and a letter[163] from Priestley to Franklin in Paris. Priestley would be vexed, for many years, that he no longer led the field in pneumatic chemistry and subsequent letters between the two 'friends', Priestley and Ingen Housz, are painfully scratchy.

1780. Calne

IN EFFECT THE AUTUMN OF 1779 had marked the end of any working relationship between Shelburne and Priestley although a further nine months would elapse before 'the Rev. Dr.' left Calne. During that time it is almost true to say that the two men remained miles apart and never saw each other: while Shelburne was in London, Priestley was in Calne, and in May 1780 the two men swapped places. The formalities of the separation appear to have taken place between April and June 1780. Before that Priestley was still wondering whether to resign or wait to be dismissed, writing to Benjamin Franklin for advice[164] shortly before 8 February (when Franklin replied). Although he avoids mentioning Shelburne by name he gives a pretty explicit picture of the rift:

> I have good reason to think that I begin to be felt as a burthen, and that the connection is no longer desirable to *him* . . . A common friend (presumably Richard Price) dates all this from our differing from *him* in political principles, but I think it has other causes . . . *His* behaviour is outwardly civil, and he makes no complaint whatever . . .

Franklin's advice[165] was to tough it out but Shelburne dismissed Priestley shortly afterwards: he would honour, though, the agreement of 1772 and would pay Priestley an annuity of £150 until death[166]. However, Shelburne, too, had been taking advice. A notion he had to set Priestley up as the director of an educational Academy in Ireland[167] was dropped but explorations how best to fund Priestley's pension continued for several months. In the end Priestley himself took the legal advice, once more, of his friend Lee and refused to accept[168] the rental income from cottages in Bremhill in lieu of cash. It is no exaggeration to say, though, that Shelburne nearly paid for his association with Priestley with his life.

In a debate in the House of Lords on 8 March Shelburne happened to make some critical comments[169] on the inappropriately rapid promotion of certain officers in the militia. As an example he quoted the case of the erstwhile secretary to Lord Stormont (Stormont had been British ambassador at Paris). This was a Scot, William Fullarton, who was now, without real qualification, a Lieutenant Colonel. Fullarton took great offence and, being an MP, stood up in the House of Commons on 20 March and made an abusive riposte directed at Lord Shelburne. Twice he was called to order for naming another parliamentarian but the interventions only made him more aggressive and he went directly from the House to write a report of his speech and submit it for publication in the next day's newspapers. Lord Shelburne, he said, was 'false, insolent and cowardly' and, what was more, 'in correspondence with the enemies of his country'. The allusion, implying treason, was to Benjamin Franklin for Fullarton and Stormont had had word of such letters from contacts at Paris. These were, of course, those of Priestley[170] Lord Shelburne himself had last communicated with Franklin in 1767[171] but it's easy to see how the truth had become distorted. In the political sphere, Priestley was personal adviser to Shelburne after all. Fullarton did not calm down overnight and, determined that Shelburne should be aware of his wrath, sent a servant to Shelburne House bearing a newspaper cutting of his speech and demanding a response. Shelburne replied:[172]

> . . . that no other answer was proper, than to desire Mr. Fullerton to meet him next morning in Hyde Park at five o'clock.

The duel, with pistols, took place: it was dawn on Wednesday 22 March. Two shots were fired to no effect but Fullarton's second shot wounded Shelburne, slightly, in the groin. Shelburne's second then asked if Fullarton was 'satisfied'. The Scotsman still demanded an apology. Shelburne protested that it was too late for regrets and that he was ready to continue. Both seconds intervened however, and disarmed the contestants. Shelburne was helped to his carriage and back to Shelburne House, to his wife, of nine months (and six months into her first pregnancy!). Happily he would recover from his injury without complications but he could probably have well done without commiserations arriving from Priestley[173], the person who had caused the 'indispensable' outing with 'providence'. If Priestley's position had not already been doomed these events would surely have been the last straw. Priestley knew it, too. He also wrote[174] to Benjamin Vaughan, one of Shelburne's younger advisers:

> I thank you for your repeated accounts of Ld. Shelburne, and am glad he is in a good way. Last night I wrote him a short letter of congratulations on his recovery, but in the present state of his mind with respect to me, I do not think that either that, or any thing else I can do, will please.

Nevertheless Shelburne's generosity was such that Priestley's liberal pension arrangements survived. In fact Priestley had spent the day of the duel in Bath, blissfully unaware that Lord Shelburne had been in such danger. By 1779 the Bath Agricultural Society was running so successfully that it had spawned another club in the town – the Bath Philosophical Society. This was formally established on 28 December 1779 and Priestley is listed as one of the founder members[175]. It's symbolic, if not significant, that Priestley appears, here, to have been acting independently of Lord Shelburne. There is no reliable record of Priestley himself having attended the inaugural gathering but he did attend at least one meeting - that of 22 March 1780 – and hence his pleasant daytrip from Calne on what was, for others, a very fateful day[176]. The 'Philosophical' fared less well than its agricultural cousin and died out a number of times over the next fifty years but eventually became securely established as the Bath Royal Literary and Scientific Institution and can still be found in Queen Square.

By the end of March 1780 Priestley was finishing off some experiments on condensation in cooling airs having received some new thermometers sent from London. He was otherwise clearing his desk, preparing to go up to Shelburne House. He had heard from Johnson[177], his publisher, that 'Disquisitions' was virtually sold out and a sheaf of unanswered correspondence that he couldn't face was the tangible result. The author of the controversial pamphlet was regretting, now, its publication and the trouble it had caused him. Despite the healthy sales he was no longer particularly fond of it and Johnson's plea for a second, revised, edition gave Priestley a heavy heart:[178]

> I have not looked it over since it was published (and) cannot, unless I be very much urged, resume the consideration of it.

Sometime in early May, Priestley went up to London. It was nearly a year since he had been there but even so he intended to stay only six weeks at Shelburne House[179]. It was his last visit there, a time to collect together his personal belongings and mothball the laboratory. It would have been his unwritten responsibility to remove any dangerous materials – fire was an ever-present danger in houses heated only by open fires and lit by candles; inflammable chemicals left to deteriorate heightened the risk of inferno. No doubt he had also planned a round of farewell meetings with his many friends – trips to London were now going to be beyond his means unless he happened to settle nearby. In the event, friends came to him: within hours of arriving he was bed bound[180]. Mary hastened from Leeds[181] to find him very ill with gallstones. He was feverish, vomiting and in great pain. Eating and drinking were repellent because of the constant nausea and Priestley knew[182] that he had a condition that was sometimes fatal. On the other hand his parlous state of health seems to have brought about a prompt reunion with Mary; indeed, a reconciliation. She efficiently nursed him back to health so that by 1 June he was agreeing plans with her to move to Birmingham. John Wilkinson[183], Mary's older brother, who lived near Wolverhampton, had arrived in London on business and went to Shelburne House[184]. He persuaded them that living in Birmingham would give them easy access to many old friends, besides he and his family, and that the cost of living there would be considerably less than in Calne[185]. As if to quell any opposition, Wilkinson also reminded Priestley that travelling could be therapeutic for sufferers of gallstones and that a coach ride to Birmingham would be just the thing to complete his recovery[186]. Being thrown around in a poorly sprung carriage as it clattered along the rough and ready roads of the eighteenth century was normally an unpleasant and unavoidable aspect of travelling but, with some irony, this nauseating experience was reckoned to be an 'exercise' that helped to 'expel' gallstones.

Whether it was the 'carriage cure' or not, Priestley was somewhat better still by 23 June when he was back in Calne[187] having found somewhere next to live, on the outskirts of Birmingham. Mary too, was reported[188] to be 'better than she has been'. The boys were soon due home from school and the family would be back together again. They could set about packing with their immediate future resolved. The only downside to Priestley's life, as he saw it[189], was the fact that he was once again deprived of time in the laboratory:

. . . my late tedious illness and the change of my situation (has meant) the consequent interruption of all my experiments for almost the whole of the summer.

The family were packed and ready to leave Calne by late July but Priestley suffered a brief relapse of his gallbladder disease[190]. Dr. Allsup was called in and gave a guarded prognosis that was reported[191] to Lord Shelburne:

Dr. Alsup thinks he will have a difficult matter to get the better of his complaint without the greatest care as to regime.

Shelburne probably found it difficult to be too concerned. He had more immediate worries for his wife was also ill[192]. Allsup, too, had distractions from Priestley's clinical condition. He had taken time out of his practice that summer and cut the Cherhill white horse[193]. He also had an ulterior motive for visiting his patient at The Parsonage House. Knowing that the Priestleys were leaving he had approached William Essington, Shelburne's new agent at Bowood, to put in a bid to be the new tenant[194]. Allsup was seen as a very desirable occupant for he and his wife were childless and there would be 'less wear and tear' on the property[195]. After some negotiations on the rent, the house was leased to him for £20 per year[196] and he was able to move in shortly after 12 August. By then the Priestley 'goods' had already been sent[197] to Birmingham and presumably the family made haste to follow very soon after in order to be there to receive them.

Birmingham 1780 – 1791

PRIESTLEY LEFT CALNE during August 1780 but the move was protracted. He finally reported being 'settled' at Birmingham on 30 November, by which time he had both recovered from his illness and Mary was much happier. Priestley himself had been appointed one of the two ministers at the New Meeting House. The salary of £100 per year would have been inadequate by itself but he now had the security of the £150 annual pension from Lord Shelburne. The income was a necessary one. He and Mary had now been married for 18 years and their well-spaced family was growing up. Sally was now 17, Jos 12, William 9 and little Henry (Harry) 3. There were still 6 at table and many years of education to pay for.

The role of Minister to a congregation was one to which Priestley was glad to return:[198]

> . . .the capacity of a public teacher of Christianity . . . I deem to be the most truly honourable of any character, office or employment in this world.

But he had negotiated an idiosyncratic job description, preaching and teaching only on Sundays. Although the Sabbath was an extremely busy day for him, the rest of each week was his own. He quickly established a laboratory in a detached, ground-floor wing (in case of fire) of the new family home, a large rented house, 'Fair Hill', one and a half miles from the town centre. He already knew of several friends in the town and Mary had her brother, John Wilkinson, at Bilston near Wolverhampton. Several particular and long-standing acquaintances of Priestley were members of the Lunar Society of Birmingham[199], men prominent in provincial science and industry. Among them were Matthew Boulton, James Watt, Erasmus Darwin and Josiah Wedgwood. Many of the dozen or so membership lived well outside

Birmingham and the society therefore arranged their monthly meetings for the Sunday nearest the full moon, the better to see their way home, and hence their name. Within a few weeks Priestley was invited to join. In fact the established members were so keen to recruit him that they changed their meetings to Mondays to accommodate his weekly routine.

A further volume of his 'Experiments and Observations on Natural Philosophy' appeared in March 1781, two years after the first. There was sparse new material in the book and Priestley admitted that it was 'imperfect'. There was much discussion of the 'green matter' (algal growth) that always appears, sooner or later, in stagnant water. At issue was its relation to oxygen production in sunlight. His theories of what was actually happening conflicted with those of Ingen Housz but we now know that both men were misinterpreting their observations. An appendix to the book, containing several letters from his friends, was accidentally significant. John Warltire had reminded Priestley of an experiment to which he had been a witness. Warltire had passed an electric spark through a mixture of 'inflammable air' (hydrogen) and 'common air' (atmospheric air) in a sealed glass container. He had been trying to demonstrate a weight change (unsuccessfully) but had noted, consistently, that the glass walls of the chamber, clean and dry beforehand, were afterwards 'dewy'. Priestley described this simple observation as merely 'random', unlike Lavoisier who had leapt on its significance. Here we have oxygen and hydrogen combining to form water, one of the most important chemical discoveries of the era. It was one of the major building blocks of Lavoisier's 'New Chemistry': that when substances burned what was really happening was that they were combining with oxygen. Their weight, if measured very carefully, increased rather than decreased. It was a consistent finding in skilled hands such as Lavoisier's and it consigned Phlogiston to the history books. As is so often the case with scientific genius, Priestley was past his prime by the age of 50. Although there were to be several further letters published by the Royal Society and a yet further volume of Experiments and Observations, he made no further important discoveries in chemistry. In clinging to the wreckage of the Phlogiston theory, his scientific writings were now looking irrelevant. One might even say that Priestley's scientific career burst rather than petered out. In 1784 the new craze for ballooning arrived in Birmingham. Priestley and other Lunar Society members set about making a hydrogen balloon as invented at Paris by the French chemist, Jacques Charles. Their balloon, launched in January 1785, hit a tree and punctured. It deflated immediately and so did the enthusiasm of its makers. It was a symbolic failure for Priestley.

In July 1782 Lord Shelburne had unexpectedly become Prime Minister on the sudden death of Lord Rockingham. What Priestley thought about having missed out on a life so close to the ultimate seat of political power is nowhere recorded. It can be assumed, though, that he was pleased to see how a peace was brokered with the Americans on Shelburne's 'watch'. It must have satisfied him, also, that the chief American negotiator had been his other old friend, Franklin, still at Paris. Shelburne was made first Marquis of Lansdowne for his successes. Priestley himself was now more focussed on civic activities and politics in Birmingham. In 1782 he reorganised the town's subscription library along the lines that he had pioneered at Leeds. In 1784 the Sunday School movement, started at Gloucester in 1781 by the journalist, Robert Raikes, spread to Birmingham. These were not meant to be religious institutions but provide a basic education for the children of the illiterate poor who otherwise terrorised the streets on Sundays. It was usual for the pupils to attend church for an hour during the afternoon. Priestley led a Dissenters protest in Birmingham, a resistance against such services being held only in orthodox churches. The protest eventually prevailed when it was agreed that the children of nonconformists could attend their own chapels and Sunday Schools in Birmingham were thereafter a considerable success. Home life in 1784 was not so gratifying. Sally was very ill with rheumatic fever and it took her a long time to recover. However, she was able to marry, on 17 January 1786, William Finch, a struggling ironmaster and nail-maker.

Released from the tacit restraints of working for Lord Shelburne there was an explosion of religious publications – over 50 between 1784 and 1789, many of which had very political overtones. Priestley became the best-known propagandist of the opponents to the reviled 'Test Acts' that gave conforming Anglicans huge privileges in society. He remained a theological wild card. Not for him the 'live and let live' attitude that so often goes hand in hand with advancing years. By the end of 1782 he had published a huge tome, in two volumes, called 'History of the corruptions of Christianity'. This was a compendium of radical and provocative theological thinking; a useful reference work where the growing number of his enemies could find ammunition. In late 1787 he began a new English translation of The Bible, he working on the Old Testament and his friend, Lindsey, on the New. The work mushroomed and various sections were seconded, piece-meal, to a long list of other friends and colleagues, Priestley growing into the role of editor. By repute it began to take on the guise of the 'Unitarian' Bible but much of the enormous multiple effort was to come to a sad and very abrupt end. He also began to accept more and more invitations to give sermons to distant congregations, in Leeds and London (annually at Hackney for his old friend Richard Price) and even, occasionally, in Calne. Many of these sermons found their way into print. Some of them were trenchant presentations of very controversial views seen as apostate, Priestley using the pulpit as an orange box. A provocative 'anti-slavery' sermon was published in 1788 and in a memorial sermon at Hackney after Richard Price's death in April 1791, Priestley praised the French Revolution which had 'emancipated our neighbours' from their 'undemocratic government'.

Priestley was far from alone in supporting the French Revolution and in saying so. In fact the majority of literate society voiced their initial approval of what was happening across the English Channel. However, the cataclysmic events of 14 July 1789, seen to hold out such promise, merely led from one kind of tyranny to another. The new one was more violent, more sickening and more threatening. Public opinion did a prompt U-turn but, characteristically, Priestley did not. Here was a stick with which reactionary elements could beat him. On Monday 11 July 1791 an advertisement appeared in the Birmingham Gazette that 'The Friends of Freedom' were to hold a dinner, on the 14th, at three in the afternoon, to celebrate the second anniversary of the storming of the Bastille prison in Paris, the beginning of the French Revolution. Some 80 diners attended a central Birmingham hotel and were heckled on their way in. Priestley did not turn up, though fully expected, and the crowd seemed at a loss and dispersed. By eight in the evening they had reassembled and their mood was obviously ugly. They became a riotous mob that set upon various buildings in the town. The trail of destruction was far from random – New Meeting House was destroyed, Old Meeting House very badly damaged and then the mob made directly for Priestley's own house which was ransacked and set on fire. Fortunately the threat of serious violence had been 'telegraphed' to several of Priestley's close friends, yet more evidence that the events were far from spontaneous. As the mob, sworn to kill him, approached Fair Hill, he and his family were persuaded to flee, finding safe refuge, eventually, at Heath Forge with their daughter and son-in-law. They very quickly moved on to London. In the meantime the

'Church and King' riots continued for two further days while the local Magistrates rejected military intervention and someone threw away the key to the fire engine hut. A further two Meeting Houses and 26 private homes were destroyed and anyone that the mob might choose to label as a 'd ——d Presbyterian' feared for their safety. Priestley's response to these events was courageous but foolhardy verging on suicidal. Within days he was planning to return to Birmingham to give a sermon in the ruins of the New Meeting House based on the text 'Forgive them, Father, for they know not what they do.' Fortunately his London friends dissuaded him of this madness, for the sake of his family at least, and Mary Priestley was adamant that she and the children would never, ever, revisit the town. So, at the age of 58, Priestley had to accept that he had lost not only his home, his laboratory, his apparatus, his books and his manuscripts, but also his occupation.

London 1791 – 1794

IN LONDON Priestley and his family drifted through the homes of several sympathetic friends until, in October, they again rented a house of their own in Clapton, just north of Hackney. In November Priestley accepted an invitation to become the morning preacher at the Gravel Pit Meeting House at Hackney, effectively succeeding Richard Price. The annual salary was 150 guineas and his first sermon was given on Sunday 4 December. His scientific activities were restricted, necessarily, to conducting disputatious correspondence with other philosophers, although Sir Joseph Banks, now President of the Royal Society, sent him some valuable chemicals to try to encourage him back to the laboratory bench. But his life as an effective experimental scientist seemed finished. He did, however, give a series of memorable lectures on 'Experimental Philosophy' at New College, Hackney, a brief resumption of his earlier life as a teacher at a Dissenting Academy. Not that it helped him personally. 'Hackney' college was seen as a revolutionary hotbed, its students having pointedly invited Tom Paine to lecture to them. Priestley's association was probably one of the reasons that his name was added to the 1792 Home Office list of 'disaffected and seditious persons'.

Within six months, then, of losing everything at Birmingham, Priestley had reassembled the structure of his life and might have been content to work his way back to social tolerance. Mary and the boys, however, were much more disorientated by the enforced retreat to London. Mary had lost her circle of friends again and plans for Jos and William to take up commercial careers fell apart when the Priestley name lost its respectability. William visited France with his uncle and thought to settle there until the declaration of war in February 1793. In desperation Priestley wrote to U. S. Vice-President, John Adams, whom he had met while Adams had been envoy to London 1785-8, asking advice about emigrating to the United States. Adams wrote a rather cautious reply but William's decision had already been made. He sailed to America directly from France. Then Jos and Harry sailed from England to join him. Mary was determined not to lose her sons even if it meant crossing the Atlantic and parting from Sally and the grandchildren. Her husband remained reluctant for added reasons. He feared that Mary's continual dry cough and slow wasting represented consumption (tuberculosis) and that she would not survive the journey. More selfishly he knew he would lose all possibility of restoring his former intimacies with the British scientific establishment, the Royal Society and its clubs. The conflict was resolved largely by Mary's iron will and by a growing sense of isolation and persecution for Priestley himself. They were among some 10,000 people who emigrated to America in 1794, a huge proportion being 'liberal thinkers' from England.

JOSEPH PRIESTLEY HOUSE, NORTHUMBERLAND, PENNSYLVANIA (Courtesy of the Joseph Priestley House, Northumberland, PA., USA.)
The southern aspect of the large house overlooking the Susquehannah River at Northumberland, Pennsylvania. Mary Priestley played the dominant role in designing the house but died before building was completed in 1798. Priestley died, in February 1804, in the room to the right of the door.

America 1794 – 1804

THE PRIESTLEYS spent March 1794 in packing their few remaining possessions and in saying their farewells before sailing on Tuesday 8 April. After eight nauseating weeks at sea (Mary wrote to a friend of very strong winds and icebergs) their ship stood off New York waiting for a pilot. To their joy a private boat brought Jos out to meet them and fetch them to a boarding house. It was Wednesday 4 June 1794. The first adjustment the Priestleys had to make to life in America was to celebrity status. George Clinton, Governor of New York, was an early visitor and they dined with him several times. They left for Philadelphia, to join their other sons, on 18 June, and there, too, were received publicly and enthusiastically. Sadly Benjamin Franklin had died four years earlier but any long-standing friend of the local hero was due a warm reception. And in early July Priestley even took tea with George Washington.

Although circumstances had virtually forced Priestley to emigrate to America against his will he had come to terms with the reality and had had very positive thoughts. He now set about trying to realise substantial plans for a new life. He wanted to found a freethinking 'utopia' for radical émigrés like himself where he might be both pastor and schoolmaster. He rejected several eminent positions offered to him in Philadelphia, seeing the isolation of Northumberland, a 'backwoods' settlement 130 miles to the northwest, as a likely place to establish his 'radical' community and Jos had already bought land there. Although the town never became the safe haven for liberal thinkers and dissenting believers that he had conceived, it became the new Priestley home. There were fewer than 100 houses and plenty of building plots for sale. Priestley bought five adjacent 'lots' that overlooked the Susquehanna River and began to have a house built to a plan of Mary's. It was not fully completed until 1798. In the meantime they lived with Jos and then in a rented house in the town. On Friday 11 December 1795 Harry died, probably of malaria. Then, on Saturday 17 September 1796, Mary Priestley also died; her grief and her consumption overwhelming her. Priestley, now a lonely man of 63, finally moved into his new house in early 1797, although he had been able to use the laboratory wing from 1796. Unhappily his scientific work was ineffective, his experiments largely irrelevant since they were still all based on outmoded theories involving phlogiston. Indeed, a new flood of scientific papers was almost completely motivated by his stubborn resistance to the 'new' chemistry that rightly became the basis of modern science we know today.

Despite frequent pleas, in writing, that Sally join him in America, Priestley was never to see his daughter again. She died – also of consumption – in June 1803, leaving five daughters and two sons. Jos eventually returned to England where he died in 1833. William settled in Louisiana, having made a fortune in land speculation and died in 1840. Until a debilitating bout of pleurisy in 1801, Priestley himself remained as active as ever, visiting Philadelphia annually and keeping up a busy schedule of writings on theology, and giving lectures and sermons. His subsequent debility confined him to reading and writing until, on the morning of Monday 6 February 1804, he just lay back, closed his eyes and died: a life that had been so full of struggle and fraught with controversy ended so peacefully that Jos and his wife, in the room at the time, didn't realise for some minutes.

JOSEPH PRIESTLEY IN OLD AGE
(Courtesy of the Royal Society Library, London).
A photograph, taken in the 1860s, of a tinted drawing of Priestley, as an older man, when living in America. There he abandoned the habit of wearing a wig and his own hairline is shown together with the facial features we see, consistently, in images of the younger man.

Postscript

Notices of Priestley's death appeared in England in mid-April 1804. The congregation at the rebuilt New Meeting House in Birmingham wore mourning apparel for two months and a memorial sermon was preached at Mill Hill Chapel in Leeds. There is no evidence of any such public grieving at Bowood or in Calne but there were individuals who had reason to brood over the passing of a man who had so changed their lives. Both of the Sewell sisters from Leeds had remained in the town even though the Priestleys had left, to go to Birmingham, 23 years earlier. We've seen how Mary Sewell, the older sister, had married a Calne baker, a young man called Joseph Perkins, in 1775, and that the first child came along uncomfortably quickly. The couple went on to build a successful Calne business together, eventually running their own bakery and grocery shop in Church Street[200]. After James and Thomas, baptised together on 8 June 1777, the Perkins also went on to have a further 10 children between 1778 and 1792[201]. These did not all survive but by the 1790s the house and shop in Church Street must have been bursting at the seams. Joseph Perkins died in 1805 but the shop remained open, run by his widow and some of the sons. Two of the daughters in particular, Mary Perkins (born 7 December 1781) and Sophia Perkins (born 29 March 1785) are especially important in Calne's history.

On Sunday 29 May 1808, Mary junior married John Harris, a 23-year old butcher, also born in Church Street. The groom was the eldest son of a John Harris who had come to Calne with his mother, Sarah, in 1770, to open a new butcher's shop. John senior had died, however, in 1791 and, rather in parallel with the Perkins's establishment, the Harris butchery shop was now also being run by the widow and the children. John junior, though, had recently used, on reaching his majority, a £20 inheritance from his

Grandmother, Sarah (died 1794) to open his own butcher's shop on the corner of High Street and Church Street where, in a small way, he began curing bacon. This became the home for Mary (née Perkins), his new wife, in 1808. And the bond between the Perkins and Harris families became even stronger when Henry Harris, John's youngest brother, married Sophia Perkins in 1812, about a year after Mary Perkins senior (née Sewell) had died. These newlyweds took over the (now failing) grocery/bakery shop under the Harris name and also began curing bacon. Here were the beginnings of a dynasty. The name 'Harris' was to become synonymous with Calne and the UK bacon industry and the Harris family were to become very rich and famous – the 'Harristocracy'. Mary Priestley had brought her two friends, the sisters Mary and Elizabeth Sewell from Leeds for her own motives, for female company and friendship. But she had also brought, to Calne, some fresh 'blood' which helped to feed a whole new river of enterprise that would supplant the declining woollen industry; the more so since we haven't, yet, considered the subsequent story of the younger Sewell sister.

Elizabeth Sewell had been just approaching her 14th birthday when she arrived in Calne in 1774 and though still only 21 in 1780, when the Priestleys left the town, she also seems to have remained behind. The next surviving record of her in Calne is her name in the marriage register of St. Mary's Church for 1785. On Thursday 9 June – two days after her 25th birthday – she married Robert Waterman, a blacksmith from an extensive Calne family. Children soon came along. Sons, Samuel, Charles and Robert were born in 1786, 1789 and 1792 respectively and then, on 28 January 1795, Elizabeth was delivered of a daughter baptized, also, Elizabeth. She, twenty years later, in the summer of 1815, married, at St. Mary's Church, on Thursday 1 June, William Maundrell. The Maundrells were another prominent Calne family; William had a farm at Knight's Marsh on the southernmost outskirts of the town. William and Elizabeth went on to have a large family – seven children were born between 1816 and 1829. And among their many Maundrell cousins was one called Edward who, in the 1850s, fathered Edward Ward Maundrell. 'E W', as he was universally known, grew up to create the famous Calne iron foundry at Horsebrook where, to complete the circle, some of the machinery used in the Harris factory was devised and cast. By lineage, or at least by linkage, the Sewell girls who had kept Mary Priestley company and offset her isolation and homesickness turn out to be an important thread in the history of Calne. Indeed, one might say that the full legacy of the Priestleys' seven years in the town is as much human and economic as scientific. Perhaps if there were to be a statue in Calne it ought to be of Mary Priestley. Now, there's a piece of lateral thinking that's worthy of Priestley himself.

THE PRIESTLEY MEMORIAL, CHURCH STREET, CALNE

The memorial to Joseph Priestley designed by David Reeves and assembled by Calne Artists Group in 2000/1 as part of the 'Breath of Life' theme taken for the town centre refurbishment. The central bronze head of Priestley, modelled by Vivien ap Rhys Pryce, is surrounded by alchemical symbols of all the common elements.

Notes and References

1 Priestley J. *The history and present state of electricity*. London, J. Johnson 1767.

2 Letter, J Priestley to Dr. Richard Price, 2 July 1772. Rutt J. *Life and correspondence of Joseph Priestley, LL.D., F.R.S.* London, R Hunter, 1831. Volume 1, p. 175.

3 Letter, J Priestley to Dr. Richard Price, 25 August 1772. Rutt J. *op. cit.* Volume 1, p. 178.

4 Letter, Benjamin Franklin to Joseph Priestley 19 September 1772. Rutt J. *op. cit.* Volume 1, p. 182.

5 Schofield R. *The enlightened Joseph Priestley*. University Park, PA., The Pennsylvania State University Press, 2004. p. 93.

6 Schofield R. *The enlightenment of Joseph Priestley*. University Park, PA., The Pennsylvania State University Press, 1997. p.271.

7 Letter, J Priestley to William Turner 18 July 1773. Royal Society manuscripts, 654, XV–b–6.

8 Wiltshire County Reference Library. Wiltshire Listed Buildings: The White Hart, Calne.

9 Wiltshire and Swindon History Centre 1312/6. Calne parish accounts (poor book) 1757–1785.

10 Wiltshire and Swindon History Centre. Transcribed burial register, St. Andrew's Church, Heddington, near Calne.

11 Wiltshire and Swindon History Centre. 1312/6: Calne parish accounts (poor book) 1757–1785.

12 Letter, Henry Merewether to Lord Shelburne 19 May 1774. Bowood: letters 1756-1774.

13 Letter, J Priestley to William Turner 18 July 1773. Royal Society manuscripts, 654, XV–b–6.

14 Ibid.

15 Ibid.

16 A reverse extrapolation – in 1801 it was 3767 as quoted in: Fletcher A. (Ed.) *The Victoria History of the counties of England: Wiltshire. Vol XVII. Calne Hundred.* Woodbridge, Boydell & Brewer 2002. p. 32.

17 Fletcher A. (Ed.) *op. cit.* p.109.

18 Wiltshire and Swindon History Centre. Harris History: undated document produced by C & T Harris. Wiltshire Local Studies; CAL 665.

19 Letter, J Priestley to Lord John Fitzmaurice, 7 September 1774. Rutt J.*op. cit.* Volume 1, p. 240.

20 Kerry, Earl of. King's Bowood Park. *Wiltshire Archeological Magazine* Vol. XLI, June 1922. pp. 512,513.

21 Letter, J Priestley to Theophilus Lindsey, August or September 1772. Rutt J. *op. cit.* Volume 1, p. 179.

22 Gordon, A, Mercer, M. Jervis, Thomas (1748-1833), *Oxford Dictionary of National Biography* (2004). online edition, accessed Jan 2008.

23 Jervis T. In *Literary recollections of Rev. Richard Warner.* London, R. Hunter 1831. p. 13.

24 Pevsner N. *Wiltshire.* Harmondsworth, Penguin Books 1963. Reprinted 1981. p.121.

25 Letter, J Priestley to William Turner 18 July 1773. Royal Society manuscripts, 654, XV–b–6.

26 Schofield, R. *A scientific autobiography of Joseph Priestley.* Cambridge, Massachusetts. MIT Press 1966. p. 141.

27 Ibid.

28 Letter, J Priestley to Caleb Rotherham. 25 March 1774. Rutt J. *op.cit.* Volume 1, p. 228.

29 Letter, J Priestley to William Turner 18 July 1773. Royal Society manuscripts, 654, XV–b–6.

30 Letter, J Priestley to William Turner 19 February 1774. Rutt J. *op. cit.* Volume 1, p. 223.

31 Wiltshire and Swindon History Centre. 2140/119: assorted papers concerning the firm of C & T Harris, Calne and of the Harris family.

32 West Yorkshire Archive Service,Wakefield. RDP68: Registry of Deeds. Baptisms at St. Peter's Church, Leeds

33 Bowood: Shelburne, misc. corres. M–Z (Priestley).

34 In the autumn of 1773 the taxes levied on tea imported into the American colonies by the British East India Company were changed, by Parliament, much to the financial detriment of the colonists. On Thursday 16 December, as a symbolic (but expensive) protest, men dressed as native Indians boarded three ships in Boston harbour and dumped their cargos of tea into the harbour.

35 Brands H. *The first American*. New York, Doubleday, 2000. p. 467 passim.

36 Ibid. p. 469.

37 Ibid. p. 482.

38 Rutt J. *op. cit.* Volume 1, p.212.

39 Schofield R. *op. cit*, 2004. p.26.

40 Ibid.

41 Letter, Henry Merewether to Lord Shelburne 19 May 1774. Bowood: letters 1756–1774.

42 An official who controls domestic affairs of a household, directing the domestics and controlling expenditure.

43 Letter, Henry Merewether to Lord Shelburne 19 May 1774. Bowood: letters 1756–1774.

44 Ibid.

45 Fletcher A. (Ed.) *The Victoria History of the counties of England. Wiltshire: Vol XVII, Calne Hundred*. Woodbridge, Boydell & Brewer 2002. p.103.

46 Letter, Henry Merewether to Lord Shelburne 19 May 1774. Bowood: letters 1756–1774.

47 Priestley J. *Experiments and Observations on different kinds of air Vol II*. London, J. Johnson 1776. Second edition preface, p.viii.

48 Bowood: Shelburne misc. corres. M-Z (Priestley) [equivalent, now, to over £500].

49 Priestley J. *Experiments and Observations on different kinds of air* Vol II. London, J. Johnson 1776. Second edition, pp 33-34.

50 Ibid.

51 Letter, J Priestley to Hon. William Petty, 26 August 1774. Rutt J. *op. cit.* Volume 1, p. 237 passim.

52 Letter, J Priestley to Lord John Fitzmaurice, 6 September 1774. Rutt J.*op. cit* Volume 1, p. 240 passim.

53 Letter J Priestley to Hon. William Petty, 6 October 1774. Rutt J. *op. cit.* Volume 1, p. 242 passim.

54 Nothing has changed here, then.

55 John Magellan was a Portuguese monk, descendant of Ferdinando Magalhaens, discoverer of the Magellan Straits. Magellan was a self-appointed scientific 'spy' and made little secret of the fact, scuttling backwards and forwards between London and Paris, trading in the latest scientific news.

56 Letter, J Priestley to Theophilus Lindsey 21 October 1774 – quoted in a letter from Lindsey to Mr. Jebb October 29 1774. *Memoirs of Dr. Joseph Priestley, written by himself, with a continuation, to the time of his decease, by his son Joseph*. London, J Johnson 1806-1807. p.237.

57 Letter, J Priestley to Theophilus Lindsey 21 October 1774. Rutt J. *op. cit.* Volume 1, p. 251.

58 Ibid.

59 The two MPs returned for the Borough of Calne, sponsored by Lord Shelburne, were Isaac Barré and John Dunning. Marsh A. *A history of the borough and town of Calne*. Calne. R Heath 1903. p. 343.

60 Letter, J Priestley to Daniel Bull 6 October 1774. Bowood: letters 1756–1774.

61 Letter, Theophilus Lindsey to William Turner 3 November 1774. Rutt J.*op. cit.* Volume 1, p. 252.

62 Ibid.

63 Letter, J Priestley to Jeremy Bentham 16 December 1774. Schofield, R. *op. cit.* 1966. p. 146.

64 Schofield R. *op. cit*, 2004. p. 110 passim.

65 Letter, J Priestley to Richard Price 1 April 1775 (read to The Royal Society on 6 April 1775). *Journal Book (Copy) of the Royal Society* XXVIII, 1774–1777, p.233.

66 Priestley J. *Experiments and Observations on different kinds of air Vol II*. London, J. Johnson 1776. Second edition, p. 102.

67 *Journal Book (Copy) of the Royal Society*, Volume XXVIII, 1774–1777. p.221.

68 Ibid.

69 *Journal Book (Copy) of the Royal Society*, Volume XXVIII, 1774–1777. p.223.

70 *Philosophical Transactions of the Royal Society* 1775, Volume 65, pp 384-394.

71 Priestley J. *Experiments and observations on different kinds of air Vol II*. London, J. Johnson, 1776.

72 Scheele C. *Chemische abhandlung von der luft und dem feuer*. (Chemical treatise on air and fire). Bergman. Upsala und Leipzig 1777.

73 Letter, J Priestley to Theophilus Lindsey 25 March 1775. . Rutt J. *op. cit.* Volume 1, p.267.

74 Wiltshire and Swindon History Centre. Transcribed marriage register for Calne, St. Mary's 1775.

75 Which he was for 22 of the 30 weeks immediately following that August.

76 Wiltshire and Swindon History Centre. Register of baptisms at Calne, St. Mary's 1777.

77 Ibid.

78 He is recorded as paying the land tax of 6/9d for 1775 - Wiltshire and Swindon History Centre. 2176/2: Calne, St. Mary the Virgin and Holy Trinity, Account and church rate book 1756–1796.

79 Letter, Henry Merewether to Lord Shelburne 19 May 1774. Bowood: letters 1756–1774.

80 Bowood: Prebend Manor of Calne Rentals 1764-1776. passim.

81 Bowood: Shelburne misc. corres. M-Z (Priestley).

82 Bowood: Prebend Manor of Calne Rentals 1764 - 1776.

83 Williamson. The Structure of Pay in Britain, 1710 - . *Research in Economic History* 7.1982. http://privatewww.essex.ac.uk/~alan/family/N-Money.html

84 Letter, J Priestley to John Calder 7 July 1775. Rutt J. *op. cit.* Volume 1, p. 269.

85 Letter, J Priestley to John Calder 17 July 1775. Rutt J. *op. cit.* Volume 1, p. 272.

86 Bowood: Shelburne misc. corres. M-Z (Priestley).

87 Letter, J Priestley to Matthew Boulton 22 October 1775. Schofield, R. *op. cit.* 1966. p.151.

88 Letter, J Priestley to Matthew Boulton 6 November 1775. Schofield, R. *op. cit.* 1966. p.152.

89 Priestley J. *Experiments and observations on different kinds of air Vol II*. London, J. Johnson, 1776.

90 Letter, Theophilus Lindsey to Mr. Jebb – note with letter, J Priestley to William Turner 24 December 1775. Rutt J. *op.cit.* Volume 1, p. 286.

91 Ibid.

92 Schofield, R. *op. cit.* 1966. p.151.

93 Lord George Germaine, 1716-1785, was Colonial Secretary in Lord North's Cabinet during the American war of independence.

94 Schofield, R. *op. cit.* 1966. p.151.

95 Letter, J Priestley to Caleb Rotherham 9 February 1776. Schofield, R. *op. cit.* 1966. p.154.

96 Letter. Theophilus Lindsey to William Turner 15 March 1776. Rutt J. *op. cit.* Volume 1, p. 291.

97 Schofield, R. *op. cit.* 1966. p.151.

98 Now a museum and scholarship centre. Franklin lodged here between 1757 and 1775. See www.benjaminfranklinhome.org

99 Letter, J Priestley to Volta 25 April 1776. Schofield, R. *op. cit.* 1966. p.157. Alessandro Volta was professor of physics at Pavia.

100 Letter, J Priestley to Landriani 24 July 1778. Schofield, R. *op. cit.* 1966. p. 164. Masilio Landriani was professor of physics at Milan.

101 Letter, J Priestley to Theophilus Lindsey 8 July 1776. Rutt J. *op. cit..* Volume 1, p. 291.

102 Letter, J Priestley to Joshua Toulmin 9 July 1776. Rutt J. *op. cit.* Volume 1, p. 293.

103 Letter, J Priestley to Lord Shelburne 11 September 1776. Bowood: Shelburne misc. corres. M-Z (Priestley).

104 Ibid.

105 Priestley J. *Disquisitions relating to Matter and Spirit*. London, J. Johnson 1777.

106 Jonathon Swift.

107 Letter, J Priestley to Rev. Cappe 13 April 1777. Rutt J. *op. cit*. Volume 1, p. 298.

108 Ibid.

109 Schofield R. *op. cit*, 2004. p. 97.

110 Roger Boscovich was an Italian Catholic priest exiled in Paris. His title, Abbé, signified his status in the Church – a priest but without the responsibilities of a parish. This was, in continental Europe, a familiar standing for academics and philosophers.

111 Letter, J Priestley to Lord Shelburne 11 September 1776. Bowood: Shelburne misc. corres. M-Z (Priestley).

112 Ibid.

113 Priestley J. Experiments and observations on different kinds of air Vol III. London, J. Johnson 1777.

114 http://www.english-heritage.org.uk

115 *Sherborne and Yeovil Mercury*, September 15, 1777

116 Letter, J Priestley to Joshua Toulmin 8 December 1776. . Rutt J. op. cit. Volume 1, p. 295.

117 It seems very likely that Jos and William were boarding pupils in a school at 40, Long Street, Devizes, (now the Museum) run by the town's Unitarian minister, John Fenner. Fenner, like Priestley, had been educated at the Daventry Academy. Wright C. Crabb Robinson's schooldays. Transactions of the Unitarian Historical Society 1975, XVI. p.1.

118 Letter, J Priestley to Richard Wray 21 January 1777. Bowood: Shelburne misc. corres. M-Z (Priestley)

119 Schiff S. *Dr. Franklin goes to France*. London, Bloomsbury 2005. p.1.

120 Letter, Theophilus Lindsey to William Turner 11 March 1777. Rutt J. *op. cit*. Volume 1, p. 298.

121 Schofield R. *op. cit*, 2004. p.8.

122 Letter, J Priestley to Alessandro Volta 6 June 1777. Schofield, R. *op. cit*. 1966. p.

159.

123 Ibid.

124 Letter, J Priestley to Caleb Rotherham April 1778. Rutt J. *op. cit*. Volume 1, p. 312.

125 Letter, J Priestley to Lord Shelburne 8 October 1777, Bowood: Shelburne misc. corres. M-Z (Priestley).

126 Letter, The Hon. William Petty to his father, Lord Shelburne, Bowood 4 October 1777. William L. Clements Library, University of Michigan. Shelburne Papers - Vol. "Mr. Petty's Letters".

127 Letter, J Priestley to Lord Shelburne 8 October 1777, Bowood: Shelburne misc. corres. M-Z (Priestley).

128 Jervis T. (Remarks on some passages in) *Literary recollections of Rev. Richard Warner*. London, Hunter 1831. passim.

129 A meal taken in mid-afternoon at this point in the eighteenth century.

130 Bowood: letters 1775-1792.

131 Letter, J Priestley to Lord Shelburne 25 March 1778. Bowood: Shelburne misc. corres. M-Z (Priestley).

132 Letter, J Priestley to Marsilio Landriani 24 July 1778. Schofield, R. *op. cit*. 1966. p. 165.

133 Letter, J Priestley to Giovanni Fabroni 20 June 1779. Schofield, R. *op. cit*. 1966. p. 171.

134 Letter, J Priestley to Marsilio Landriani 24 July 1778. Schofield, R. *op. cit*. 1966. p. 165.

135 Letter, J Priestley to Lord Shelburne 30 December 1778. Bowood: Shelburne misc. corres. M-Z (Priestley).

136 Letter, Richard Wall to Lord Shelburne 9 September 1779. Bowood: Shelburne misc. corres. M-Z.

137 Letter, J Priestley to Caleb Rotherham April 1778. Rutt J. *op. cit*. Volume 1, p. 31.

138 Letter, J Priestley to Roger Boscovich 19 August 1778. Schofield, R. *op. cit*. 1966. p. 166. passim.

139 Bowood: Shelburne misc. corres. M-Z (Priestley).

140 Ibid.

141 Letter, J Priestley to Benjamin Franklin 27 September 1779. Schofield, R. *op. cit*. 1966. p. 178.

142 John Fothergill was a Quaker physician in London.

143. *The memoirs of Dr. Joseph Priestley, to the year 1795, written by himself,* quoted in Schofield, R. *op. cit.* 1966. p. 140.

144 Letter, J Priestley to Mr. Cross 6 January 1779. Bowood: Shelburne misc. corres. M-Z (Priestley).

145 Letter, J Priestley to Lord Shelburne 12 May 1779. Bowood: Shelburne misc. corres. M-Z (Priestley).

146 Ibid.

147 www.wirksworth.org.uk/A14WEATH. htm

148 Letter, J Priestley to Giovanni Fabbroni 20 June 1779 Schofield, R. *op. cit.* 1966. p. 171. Fabbroni was scientific assistant to Felice Fontana at Florence where he promoted scientific agriculture. Later director of the Florentine Mint.

149 Ibid.

150 Letter, J Priestley to Joseph Bretland 5 August 1779. Rutt J. *op. cit.* p. 324.

151 Gemeentearchief Breda, IV. Collectie Ingen Housz 16, A – 8.

152 Ibid.

153 Letter, Theophilus Lindsey to William Turner 22 July 1779. Rutt J. *op. cit.* Volume I, p. 320.

154 Letter, J Priestley to Caleb Rotherham 4 August 1779. Rutt J. *op. cit.* Volume 1, p. 323.

155 Fitzmaurice, E. *Life of William, Earl of Shelburne.* Volume III 1776–1805. London, Macmillan 1876. p.52 passim.

156 Letter, J Priestley to Radcliffe Scholefield 14 September 1779. Schofield, R. *op. cit.* 1966. p. 177.

157 Gemeentearchief Breda, IV. Collectie Ingen Housz 16, A – 8.

158 It had been Pringle, as Royal Physician in London, who had recommended Ingen Housz as smallpox inoculator to the Imperial Court at Vienna in 1768.

159 Ingen Housz thereafter returned to Vienna via Paris and Pringle died, in London, in January 1782.

160 Letter, J Ingen Housz to William Hunter 17 April 1782. Hunter papers H335, Glasgow University, Letter no. 478.

161 Ingen Housz J. *Experiments upon Vegetables, discovering their great power of purifying the common air in the sunshine.* London, Elmsley 1779. The book was dedicated to Sir John Pringle.

162 As he was wont to spell it. The house would, in a later era, become his second home and he died there in 1799, to be buried in Calne.

163 Letter, J Priestley to Benjamin Franklin 27 September 1779 (referred to in letter Benjamin Franklin to J Priestley 8 February 1780. Benjamin Franklin papers, American Philosophical Society.)

164 Letter, J Priestley to Benjamin Franklin (undated). Benjamin Franklin papers, American Philosophical Society.

165 Letter, Benjamin Franklin to Priestley 8 February 1780. Benjamin Franklin papers, Library of Congress.

166 Letter, J Priestley to Benjamin Franklin 21 December 1780. Benjamin Franklin papers, American Philosophical Society.

167 Ibid.

168 Letter, William Essington to Lord Shelburne 5 August 1780. Bowood: letters 1776-1792.

169 Fitzmaurice, E. *Life of William, Earl of Shelburne.* Volume III 1776–1805. London, Macmillan 1876. p.75 passim.

170 Priestley is known to have written letters to Benjamin Franklin on 13 December 1777, 11 March 1779, 8 May 1779, 27 September 1779 and in January 1780. www.franklinpapers.org/franklin

171 Shelburne wrote to Benjamin Franklin on 6 April 1782 commenting that it was pleasing to recommence a correspondence that had been interrupted in 1767. www.franklinpapers.org/franklin

172 Fitzmaurice, E. *Life of William, Earl of Shelburne.* Volume III 1776–1805. London, Macmillan 1876. p.76.

173 Letter, J Priestley to Lord Shelburne 25 March 1780. Bowood: Shelburne misc.corres. M-Z (Priestley).

174 Letter, J Priestley to Benjamin Vaughan 26 March 1780. Schofield, R. *op. cit.* 1966. p. 181.

175 Williams W, Stoddart D. *Bath – some*

encounters with science. Kingsmead, Bath 1978. p.69.

176 Ibid. p.70.

177 Letter, J Priestley to Joseph Bretland 2 April 1780. Rutt J. *op. cit.* Volume 1, p. 332.

178 Ibid.

179 Ibid.

180 Letter, J Priestley to Rev. Ashdown June 1780. Rutt J. *op. cit.* Volume 1, p. 335.

181 Letter, J Priestley to Radcliffe Scholefield 1 June 1780. . Rutt J. *op. cit.* Volume 1, p. 334.

182 Letter, J Priestley to George Scott, Philadelphia 1 September 1780. Benjamin Franklin papers, American Philosophical Society.

183 'Iron Mad' Wilkinson (1728–1808) was an industrialist working in iron and steel, his main line of business in making cannons for the Board of Ordnance. He later produced many of the cylinders for the famous steam engines of Boulton and Watt. When he died he was buried, by his wish, in an iron coffin.

184 Letter, J Priestley to Radcliffe Scholefield 1 June 1780. . Rutt J. *op. cit.* Volume 1, p. 334.

185 Ibid.

186 Ibid.

187 Letter, J Priestley to Joseph Bretland 23 June 1780. Rutt J. *op. cit.* Volume 1, p. 336.

188 Ibid.

189 Letter, J Priestley to Richard Kirwan August 1780. Schofield, R. *op. cit.* 1966. p. 182.

190 Letter, William Essington to Lord Shelburne 5 August 1780. Bowood: letters 1775-1792.

191 Ibid.

192 Letter, William Essington to Lord Shelburne 12 August 1780. Bowood: letters 1775-1792.

193 Plenderleath W. *The white horses of the west of England.* Calne, Alfred Heath 1886. p. 14.

194 Letter, William Essington to Lord Shelburne 5 August 1780. Bowood: letters 1775-1792.

195 Letter, William Essington to Lord Shelburne 12 August 1780. Bowood: letters 1775-1792.

196 Wiltshire and Swindon History Centre. 212B, 1549. Counterpart of a lease on the Parsonage House, Calne 19 March 1781.

197 Letter, William Essington to Lord Shelburne 12 August 1780. Bowood: letters 1775-1792.

198 Schofield R. *The enlightened Joseph Priestley.* University Park, PA, The Pennsylvania State University Press, 2004. p. 147.

199 Uglow J. *The Lunar Men.* Faber and Faber, London 2002.

200 Wiltshire and Swindon History Centre 2267/27.

201 These, and subsequent, baptisms, marriages and burials are all recorded in the (transcribed) registers for St. Mary the Virgin, Calne at Wiltshire and Swindon History Centre.

Appendix

Priestley's Publications during his time in Calne

An address to Protestant Dissenters of all Denominations on the Approaching Election of Members of Parliament, with respect to the state of Public Liberty in General, and of American Affairs in Particular.
London: J. Johnson, 1774.

A Letter to a Layman, on the Subject of the Rev. Mr. Lindsey's Proposal for a Reformed English Church, upon the plan of the late Dr. Samuel Clarke.
London: J. Wilkie, 1774.

Experiments and Observations on Different Kinds of Air.
London: J. Johnson, 1774.

On the noxious Quality of the Effluvia of putrid Marshes.
Philosophical Transactions of the Royal Society 1774: Vol. 62, 90-95.

Considerations for the Use of Young Men and the Parents of Young Men.
London: J. Johnson, 1775.

An Examination of Dr. Reid's Inquiry into the Human Mind, on the Principles of Common Sense, Dr. Beattie's Essay on the Nature and Immutability of Truth, and Dr. Oswald's Appeal to Common Sense in Behalf of Religion.
London: J. Johnson 1775.

Hartley's Theory of the Human Mind on the Principle of the Association of Ideas, with Essays relating to the Subject of It.
London: J, Johnson, 1775.

Philosophical Empiricism: Containing Remarks on a Charge of Plagiarism, interspersed with various Observations relating to Different Kinds of Air.
London: J. Johnson, 1775.

An Account of further Discoveries in Air.
Philosophical Transactions of the Royal Society 1775: Vol. 65, 384-394.

Experiments and Observations on Different Kinds of Air Vol II.
London: J. Johnson, 1776.

Observations on Respiration and the Use of the Blood, in Philosophical Transactions of the Royal Society 1776: Vol. 66, 226-248.

Disquisitions relating to Matter and Spirit. To which is added, The History of the Philosophical Doctrine concerning the Origin of the Soul and the Nature of Matter, and Its Influence on Christianity, especially with Respect to the Doctrine of the Pre-existence of Christ.
London: J. Johnson, 1777.

A Harmony of the Evangelists, in Greek, to which are prefixed Critical Dissertations in English.
London: J, Johnson, 1777.

Experiments and Observations on Different Kinds of Air III.
London: J. Johnson, 1777.

A Free Discussion of the Doctrines of Materialism, and Philosophical Necessity.
London: J. Johnson and T. Cadell, 1778.

Experiments and Observations relating to various Branches of Natural Philosophy, with a Continuation of the Observations on Air.
London: J. Johnson, 1779.

A Free Address to those who have Petitioned for the Repeal of the late Act of Parliament in Favour of Roman Catholics.
London: J. Johnson, 1780.

A Harmony of the Evangalists in English; with Critical Dissertations, and Occasional Paraphrase, and Notes for the Use of the Unlearned.
London: J. Johnson, 1780.

A Letter to Jacob Bryant Esq. in Defence of the Illustrations of Philosophical Necessity.
Bath: R. Crutwell, for J. Johnson, 1780.

A Second Letter to the Rev. Mr. John Palmer, in Defence of the Illustrations of Philosophical Necessity.
London: J. Johnson, 1780.

Index

Dr Beale, recently retired, was a general practitioner in Calne, Wiltshire for 30 years. In 1988 he was awarded an MD by Cambridge University for a prize-winning dissertation, 'Unemployment and family health' following the closure of C & T Harris (bacon, pies and sausages). He also shared the James Mackenzie Prize of the Royal College of General Practitioners for the same research. Becoming an expert on epidemiology (the study of the causes and distribution of diseases) led him to an interest in local history. He has been able to appreciate this uniquely since he has a background in science combined, now, with years of exposure to the foibles of humanity and a growing confidence in reading into historical documents.

Front cover illustration

MEDALLION (Courtesy of the Royal Society Library, London).
Wedgwood medallion in jasperware after English sculptor, John Flaxman (1755-1826). Probably made shortly after 1780 when Priestley left Calne. He and Josiah Wedgwood were both members of the Lunar Society at Birmingham and would have met regularly: indeed, Wedgwood supported Priestley financially while he was in Birmingham and also made him ceramic apparatus.